100 MATHS
HOMEWORK
ACTIVITIES

YEAR 5

Yvette McDaniel and Richard Cooper

Credits

Authors
Yvette McDaniel
Richard Cooper

Development Editor
Nicola Morgan

Editor
Ruth Burns

Assistant Editor
Margaret Eaton

Illustrations
Andy Robb (Beehive Illustration)
Jon Mitchell (Beehive Illustration)

Series Designer
Helen Taylor

Designer
Macmillan Publishing Solutions

Mixed Sources
Product group from well-managed forests and other controlled sources
www.fsc.org   Cert no. TT-COC-002769
© 1996 Forest Stewardship Council

Text © Yvette McDaniel
and Richard Cooper
© 2009 Scholastic Ltd

Designed using Adobe InDesign

Published by Scholastic Ltd
Villiers House
Clarendon Avenue
Leamington Spa
Warwickshire CV32 5PR

www.scholastic.co.uk

Printed by Bell and Bain Ltd, Glasgow

1 2 3 4 5 6 7 8 9   9 0 1 2 3 4 5 6 7 8

British Library Cataloguing-in-Publication Data
A catalogue record for this book is available from the British Library.

ISBN 978-1407-10220-7

The rights of Yvette McDaniel and Richard Cooper to be identified as the authors of this work have been asserted by them in accordance with the Copyright, Designs and Patents Act 1988.

Extracts from the Primary National Strategy's *Primary Framework for Mathematics* (2006) www.standards.dfes.gov.uk/primaryframework © Crown copyright. Reproduced under the terms of the Click Use Licence.

Contents

Introduction **4-5**

Homework diary **6**

Homework

Homework: Counting, partitioning and calculating

Teachers' notes. **7-8**

Homework sheets **9-20**

Homework: Securing number facts, understanding shape

Teachers' notes. **21-22**

Homework sheets **23-40**

Homework: Handling data and measures

Teachers' notes. **41-42**

Homework sheets **43-54**

Homework: Calculating, measuring and understanding shape

Teachers' notes. **55-56**

Homework sheets **57-68**

Homework: Securing number facts, relationships and calculating

Teachers' notes. **69-70**

Homework sheets **71-88**

Puzzles and problems

Objectives grid **89**

Activities **90-107**

Answers

Homework answers. **108-110**

Puzzles and problems answers **111**

About the series

100 Maths Homework Activities offers a complete solution to your planning and resourcing for maths homework activities. There are six books in the series, one for each year group from Year 1 to Year 6.

Each *100 Maths Homework Activities* book contains 72 homework activities, which cover the Renewed Framework objectives, and 36 puzzles and problems, which focus on the Using and applying objectives.

About the homework activities

Each homework activity is presented as a photocopiable page, with some supporting notes for parents and carers provided underneath the activity. Teachers' notes relating to the activities appear in grid format at the beginning of each block's activities. When exactly the homework is set and followed up is left to your professional judgement.

Across the *100 Maths Homework Activities* series, the homework activities cover a range of homework types. Some of the activities are for sharing. These encourage the child to discuss the homework task with a parent or carer, and may, for example, involve the home context, or a game to be played with the carer. Other activities involve investigations or problem-solving tasks. Again, the parent or carer is encouraged to participate in the activity, offering support to the child, and discussing the activity and its outcomes with the child.

Using the homework activities

Each homework page includes a 'Helper note', which explains the aim of the homework and how the adult can support their child if he or she cannot get started. It is recommended that some form of homework diary be used alongside these activities, through which to establish an effective home-school dialogue about the children's enjoyment and understanding of the homework. A homework diary page is provided on page 6 of this book.

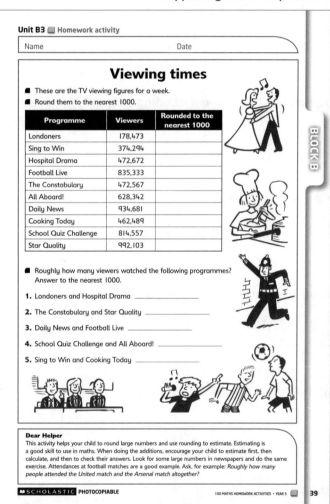

Teachers' notes

The teachers' notes appear in a grid format at the start of each block's homework activities. Each grid contains the following information:

- the Framework unit
- the homework activity's title
- a brief description of the format and content of the activity, which will help you to decide which homework activity to choose
- the Renewed Framework learning objective/s
- a 'Managing the homework' section which provides two types of help – 'before' and 'after'. The 'before' notes provide suggestions for ways to introduce and explain the homework before the children take it home. These notes might include a brief oral activity to undertake as preparation for the homework. The 'after' notes provide suggestions for how to manage the review of the homework when the children return with it to school. Suggestions include discussing strategies used for solving a problem, comparing solutions, and playing a game as a class.

About the puzzles and problems

The puzzles and problems (pages 90-107) provide coverage of the Using and applying mathematics objectives and can be used very flexibly to provide children with a comprehensive range of fun maths tasks to take home. The grid displayed on page 89 shows which puzzles and problems cover each of the Using and applying objectives.

Puzzles and problems

27 Long jump

Chaya jumped 2.26m in the long jump on sports day.

Her friend Grace jumped 83cm further.

How far did Grace jump in metres?

28 Pushbike puzzle

Tom has completed $\frac{7}{10}$ of a 50km road race.

How far has Tom got to cycle before he gets to the finish line?

SCHOLASTIC PHOTOCOPIABLE 100 MATHS HOMEWORK ACTIVITIES • YEAR 5 **103**

The puzzles and problems are based on work that the children will be covering during the year and should test their skills at that level. Some of the questions may be solved quickly, others will require more thought. Either way, children should be encouraged to try a variety of different approaches to solving problems and to look for clues and patterns in maths. It is essential for them to read the question carefully (sometimes more than once) to understand exactly what they are being asked to do. A few of the puzzles and problems will require an everyday household item or the help of a family member. Most should be readily solved by a child working on their own.

Remind the children that if a problem or puzzle is proving too difficult or frustrating, they could leave it and come back to it later with a refreshed mind!

Developing a homework policy

The homework activities have been written with the DCSF 'Homework guidelines' in mind. These can be located in detail on the Standards website **www.standards.dfes.gov. uk/homework/goodpractice** The guidelines are a good starting point for planning an effective homework policy. Effective home-school partnerships are also vital in ensuring a successful homework policy.

Encouraging home-school links

An effective working partnership between teachers and parents and carers makes a positive impact upon children's attainment in mathematics. The homework activities in this book are part of that partnership. Parents and carers are given guidance on what the homework is about, and on how to be involved with the activity. There are suggestions for helping the children who are struggling with a particular concept, such as ways of counting on or back mentally, and extension ideas for children who would benefit from slightly more advanced work.

The homework that is set across the curriculum areas for Year 5 should amount to a total of about two and a half hours a week. The homework diary page, which can be sent home with the homework activity with opportunities for a response from the parents/carers, can be found on page 6 of this book.

Using the activities with *100 Maths Framework Lessons Year 5*

The activities covered in this book fit the planning within the book *100 Maths Framework Lessons Year 5* (also published by Scholastic Ltd). As teachers plan their work on a week-by-week basis, so the homework activities can be chosen to fit the appropriate unit of work.

Name of activity & date sent home	Child's comments		Helper's comments	Teacher's comments
	Did you like this activity? Draw a face. 😊 😐 😞 a lot a little not much	How much did you learn? Draw a face. 😊 😐 😞 a lot a little not much		

Counting, partitioning and calculating

Activity name	Learning objectives	Managing the homework
A1		
Investigating place value Re-order two, three or four given digits to make as many different numbers as possible.	Explain what each digit represents in whole numbers, and partition and order these numbers	**Before:** Ask the children to remind you of the strategies used in class to find the greatest and smallest numbers. **After:** Share results. Is the outcome the same with different digits?
Aim high A place value game using five 0–9 cards to make the highest number.	Explain what each digit represents in whole numbers, and partition and order these numbers	**Before:** Discuss the place value choices children face when they pick a high or low digit early in the game. **After:** Invite the children to describe their strategies. Ask what difficult decisions they had to make (for example, a middle-sized number early on).
The differences game Subtract by counting on aloud, either mentally or using a number line.	Extend mental methods for whole-number calculations, for example to subtract one near-multiple of 1000 from another (for example, 6070 – 4097)	**Before:** Remind the children about counting on in 'jumps' to round up to the next 10, 100 and so on. **After:** Ask the children to explain how they calculated. Can they suggest a rule to help someone else?
Take it away! Practise the vertical subtraction methods used in class – the expanded or compact methods – with some calculations.	Use efficient written methods to subtract whole numbers	**Before:** Remind the children to use the method that they have been working on in class and not to be tempted to try somebody else's 'easier' method. **After:** Ask individuals to demonstrate the method(s) they prefer. Troubleshoot any difficulties.
A2		
Number chains Spot the pattern and complete the number sequence.	Count from any given number in whole-number and decimal steps, extending beyond zero when counting backwards	**Before:** Do some examples of these types of number patterns together. Discuss some strategies and things to look for. **After:** Hear some examples and invite the children to challenge each other with their own examples. Ask them to explain the 'key' or 'rule' to their patterns.
Where is the hottest place? Use < and > to order temperatures and write statements about them.	Explain what each digit represents in whole numbers and order these numbers	**Before:** Ask the children to remind you of the meanings of the < and > symbols. **After:** Link to geography. Ask: *Where would you go to ski? Where would you go to get a suntan?* Encourage the children to use an atlas to find the locations of the places listed on the worksheet.
Number search Find lines of four numbers that can be rounded to the same whole 10 or 100.	Explain what each digit represents in whole numbers and round and order these numbers	**Before:** Ask the children to remind you of the rule that they created to assist them with rounding numbers. **After:** Invite the children to share their results.
Colour, add and win Complete addition and subtraction calculations in order to colour the flowers.	Use knowledge of place value and addition and subtraction of two-digit numbers to derive sums and differences	**Before:** Establish the playing rules and demonstrate using the example on the sheet. **After:** Children swap sheets with a partner and check the calculations.

Counting, partitioning and calculating

Activity name	Learning objectives	Managing the homework
A3		
Use what you know Multiply using factors or near multiples of 10.	Recall quickly multiplication facts up to 10 × 10; use them to multiply pairs of multiples of 10 and 100	**Before:** Ask the children to explain to you what a factor is and how it can help us to multiply. **After:** Discuss the strategies used and discover preferences.
Painting by multiples Colour in a picture according to given multiples.	Recall quickly multiplication facts up to 10 × 10	**Before:** Tell the children that the picture is symmetrical and ask them to remind you what this means. **After:** Make a wall display of the pictures as attractive evidence of the children's learning.
What's left Practise division with decimal and fraction remainders to solve a range of word and number problems.	Refine and use efficient written methods to divide HTU ÷ U	**Before:** Ask the children to remind you of the system they follow to answer word problems. **After:** Share some results to try to spot difficulties.
Restaurant rip-off! Correct and perform calculations in the context of money.	Use knowledge of rounding, place value, number facts and inverse operations to estimate and check calculations	**Before:** Remind the children that they will have to check each of the calculations on the bill. **After:** Go through the answers and discuss any problems encountered.

Name	Date

Investigating place value

■ From the digits given, list all the numbers that you can possibly make.

■ List them in ascending order, smallest first.

■ How many numbers can you make with each set of digits?

Two digits

2 8 _____   6 7 _____

Three digits

4   5   9 _____

6   1   8 _____

Four digits

5   8   7   3 _____

_____

_____

_____

7   0   4   3 _____

_____

_____

_____

Dear Helper

This activity will encourage your child to think about the place value of each digit (what its value is in the number). A 5 in the units column is less in value than a 5 in the tens column, which is worth 50. If your child finds the numbers difficult to write in order, encourage them to partition each number (for example, 364 = 300 + 60 + 4) and look for the number with the smallest digit in the first column: this is the smallest number. Doing this will help your child to see the number order. If your child finds the activity easy, challenge them to find out whether the number of possible numbers they could make would be the same with different digits.

BLOCK A

Name	Date

Aim high

A game for two players.

◼ Cut out two sets of 0–9 digit cards.

☐ Shuffle them, then place them face down on the table.

☐ Ask your helper to play this game with you.

☐ The aim is to see who can make the biggest number.

☐ Take turns to choose a card and decide where to place it on your grid.

◼ Play the best of five games.

Player 1

Player 2

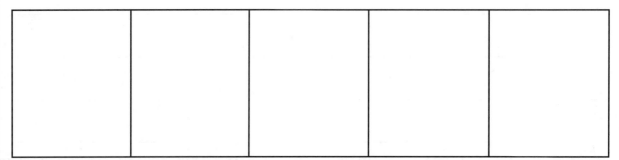

Dear Helper
Encourage your child to consider the place value of each box in the grid. From the left, the boxes are worth: tens of thousands, thousands, hundreds, tens, units. You could write TTh, Th, H, T, U above the appropriate boxes to support your child if they are finding this activity difficult. In order to get the biggest possible number, you should give any high digit you pick a high place value and give any low digit a lower place value. If your child finds this activity easy, challenge them to work out the difference between the two numbers each time.

Name	Date

The differences game

- You need a dice for this game.

  ◻ Roll a dice three or four times to generate a three-digit or four-digit number.

  ◻ The number you make must be smaller than the number in the middle of the grid.

  ◻ Write your number on the left-hand side in the spaces provided.

  ◻ Calculate the difference between the two numbers, and write it in the space on the right.

- The first one has been done for you.

Dice number

1	7	6	8

2	0	0	4
4	0	1	3
5	0	0	7
4	0	0	1
5	0	0	2
1	0	0	9
3	0	1	5
4	0	0	8
5	0	0	6

Difference

236

- Here is a number line to show the first subtraction. Draw your own number lines if they will help you to work out the other subtractions.

1768 ——+2—→ 1770 ——+30—→ 1800 ——+200—→ 2000 ——+4—→ 2004

Name	Date

Take it away!

◼ Use the written vertical method of subtraction that you have learned at school to do these calculations.

1.   H T U
  　 5 7 4
  － 3 3 2

4.   Th H T U
  　 3 5 1 4
  － 1 3 6 7

2.   H T U
  　 8 2 7
  － 4 1 4

5.   H T U
  　 8 9 2
  － 4 2 3

3.   Th H T U
  　 2 4 6 1
  － 1 3 4 7

6.   Th H T U
  　 3 5 7 9
  － 2 7 5 1

7. An outward flight to America carries 427 people. The return flight carries 579 people.

　a) What is the total number of people carried on the two flights?　＿＿＿＿＿＿＿＿＿＿

　b) What is the difference between the number of people on the outward flight and the number on the return flight?　＿＿＿＿＿＿＿＿＿＿

Dear Helper
Your child has been learning in school a variety of methods for doing written subtraction with large numbers. Encourage them to partition and redistribute the numbers, as they have been shown. Children who are having difficulty may need reminding that partitioning means: 3432 = 3000 + 400 + 30 + 2. These numbers can be redistributed, eg 3432 = 2000 + 1300 + 130 + 2 or 2000 + 1400 + 20 + 12. Also remind them to avoid taking the top number away from the bottom one by mistake. Unfortunately, the method of written subtraction that you learned at school may confuse your child. Let them teach you their method! Challenge your child to make up a five- or six-digit subtraction that needs all the digits redistributing and then solve it!

Name   Date

Number chains

◖ Can you spot the pattern in each chain?

◖ Add more links to each chain, filling in the spaces.

1.
| 1 | 1 | 1 | 2 | 1 | 1 | 1 | 2 | | | |

2.
| 3 | 3 | 2 | 1 | 3 | 3 | | | | |

3.
| 2 | 1 | 1 | 2 | 1 | 1 | | | | |

4. 18,   23,   28,   33,   38,   _____,   _____,   _____

5. 132,   122,   112,   102,   92,   _____,   _____,   _____

6. 6,   3,   0,   –3,   –6,   _____,   _____,   _____

7. 1,   2,   4,   7,   11,   16,   22,   _____,   _____,   _____

◖ Now make up some number chains of your own.

| | | | | | | | | | |

| | | | | | | | | | |

| | | | | | | | | | |

| | | | | | | | | | |

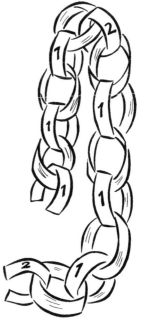

Dear Helper
Number chains can be made by adding a number each time, but they can also be made with a more complex sequence, such as a sequence of square numbers. Help your child to think about the differences between successive numbers in the chain: they do not necessarily have to be of a constant size. If your child finds the pattern difficult to see, write in the differences between the successive numbers to help them recognise a pattern. A more challenging pattern might be to double the previous number and add a constant number to it. Encourage your child to be inventive.

Name		Date	

Where is the hottest place?

◼ Use either the temperature chart below or a chart of temperatures around the world or in Britain from a newspaper.

Temperatures in °C

Amsterdam	13	London	13
Beijing	8	Los Angeles	18
Berlin	10	Malta	23
Cairo	24	Montreal	0
Cardiff	11	Moscow	–2
Corfu	20	Mumbai	34
Dublin	11	Nairobi	20
Edinburgh	10	New York	6
Florence	21	Oslo	4
Gibraltar	22	Tel Aviv	25
Guernsey	15	Toronto	5
Helsinki	–1	Vienna	6

◼ Write all the temperatures in ascending order, using the < and = symbols.

◼ Now write some sentences that compare the temperatures of different places. Write on the back of this sheet. Use words and then symbols. For example:

Helsinki is cold, but Moscow is slightly colder. –2 < –1

Corfu is cooler than Malta, which is much hotter than Vienna. 20 < 23 > 6

Dear Helper
This activity helps your child to think about positive and negative numbers on a scale. Remind your child that the bigger a negative number is, the colder the temperature is. Make sure they understand that < means 'less than' and > means 'more than'. An interesting spin-off from this activity would be to get an atlas and find these places, then think about why they are hotter or colder than other places.

Name	Date

Number search

◼ Search for lines of four numbers that would be rounded to the same nearest whole 10 or 100. For example, 16, 18, 19 and 21 would all be rounded to 20.

◼ Colour or circle the lines of numbers that you find.

16	18	19	21	385
894	141	6	204	401
59	60	61	64	399
112	138	912	249	403
897	913	933	935	226
1001	81	78	77	76
999	206	189	177	179
989	167	888	42	214
1004	188	186	194	187
566	581	612	601	26

Dear Helper

This activity helps your child to round numbers to the nearest 10 or 100. If they find the activity difficult, remind them that when we round numbers to the nearest 10, any number ending in 5 or more rounds up rather than down. So 65 rounds up to 70, but 64 rounds down to 60. Likewise, when we round to the nearest 100, any number ending in 50 or more rounds up. So 250 rounds up to 300. If your child finds the lines of numbers easily, challenge them to create a number search of their own, perhaps including decimal numbers.

BLOCK A

Name   Date

Colour, add and win

- You need some coloured pencils and a dice.
- Take it in turns to throw the dice three times.
- You must decide whether to add or subtract the numbers in order to colour one of the answer sections in the picture.
- Record your chosen sum below. The first example has been done for you.

Player 1	Player 2
6 + 5 – 2 = 9	6 + 6 + 1 = 13

Dear Helper
Encourage your child to be inventive with their mental calculations to achieve all the numbers (for example, 4 + 4 – 6 = 2). Children who have real difficulty calculating with both operations may find that having 18 counters helps, particularly when combining addition and subtraction in inventive ways in order to make a tricky number. As a challenge, ask your child to draw their own version of the pictures but number them with a selection of numbers from 12 to 108. They throw the dice three times and use any operation (including multiplication and division) in any order to make the target numbers.

Name	Date

Use what you know

◼ Use the two multiplication strategies that we have learned at school this week – finding factors and using near multiples of 10, then adjusting – to solve the following problems.

◼ Find the factors. (Remember, there may be more than one combination of factors you could try!)

For example, $12 \times 20 =$
$(6 \times 2) \times (2 \times 10) =$
$((2 \times 2) \times 6) \times 10 =$
$(4 \times 6) \times 10 =$
$24 \times 10 = 240$

12 × 18	20 × 17
24 × 15	25 × 24

◼ Use near multiples of 10.

For example, $24 \times 21 =$
just over $24 \times 20 =$
$(24 \times 2) \times 10 = 480$
and $480 + (1 \times 24) = 504$

18 × 21	18 × 19
26 × 21	26 × 19

Dear Helper
These problems help your child to use multiplication skills learned at school. Encourage your child to explain the strategies to you – this will help their understanding, and also help yours! A worked example of each strategy has been included to remind your child how to do it. If they work out these problems easily, you could stretch their skills further by challenging them to multiply by 31, 29, 41 or 39. This will involve using both strategies to find the answer.

BLOCK A

Name	Date

Painting by multiples

◼ Colour all the multiples of:

6 red   **7** blue   **8** yellow   **9** purple   **10** orange

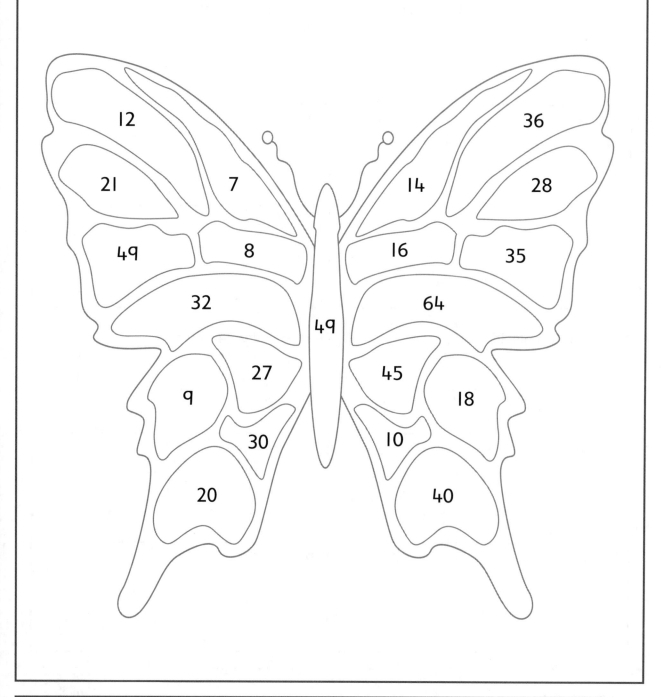

Dear Helper
This is a fun activity that will reinforce your child's knowledge of multiples and their ability to decide whether a given number is divisible by another number. If your child finds some of these multiples difficult, suggest that they write out the 6-, 7-, 8-, 9- and 10-times tables to help them. Your child might also enjoy making up a picture puzzle of this kind.

| Name | Date |

What's left?

◼ Use your division skills to solve these problems, remembering to convert your remainders to a fraction and then a decimal.

1. Alice measured 267ml of squash and decided that would be enough for four people. How much squash would each person get if it was divided exactly?	**2.** $5\overline{)417}$ $10\overline{)1079}$ $2\overline{)141}$ $4\overline{)145}$
3. Mrs Jones has bought 625cm of wood to make four shelves. How long will each shelf be if the wood is divided exactly?	**4.** I have £167 to spend over a five-day holiday. If I share the money exactly between the five days, how much can I spend on the first day?

Dear Helper

This activity helps your child to understand decimal numbers by looking at division in real-life situations where using decimals makes more sense than using remainders or fractions. We use decimals in most kinds of measures: length, money, capacity and so on. If your child is having difficulties working out the decimal, help them to find the remainder first, then find the fraction (remainder over the number they are dividing by), then relate it to a known equivalent decimal (for example, ¼ = 0.25). Challenge your child to answer the following question: *If the answer to a division question is 34.25, what could the question be?* Try to think of three different questions.

BLOCK A

Name   Date

Restaurant rip-off!

The Fat Goose

■ This is a bill for a group of seven people who ate at The Fat Goose restaurant. The waiter calculated it incorrectly! Can you spot the mistakes and calculate it correctly?

7 × cocktails @ £3.50 = £25
6 × mineral water @ £1.75 = £10.50
1 × fruit juice @ £1.90 = 90p
5 × set menu @ £23.99 = £112.95
2 × set menu @ £15.95 = £31.80
2 × wine @ £14.65 = £29.30

1. What is the correct total for the bill?

Service @ £22.95

_____

2. Once the waiter has corrected the bill, four of the people decide to split it equally. How much do they pay each?

Total = £250

_____

Dear Helper
This activity helps your child to estimate and check calculations. Your child will need to check each calculation very carefully to spot the mistakes. Encourage them to work methodically and use a systematic approach.

Securing number facts, understanding shape

Activity name	Learning objectives	Managing the homework
B1		
Times-table challenge Children time their completion of differentiated multiplication grids.	Recall quickly multiplication facts up to 10 × 10	**Before:** Stress the importance of instant recall, which means that children should not have to work out times-table facts. **After:** Record best times for future comparison. Invite the children to say some times-table fact questions for others to recall.
Sorting triangles Sort the triangles. Can a scalene triangle also be a right-angled triangle?	Identify, visualise and describe properties of triangles	**Before:** Ask the children to tell you some properties for each of the three types of triangles. **After:** Ask the children how many of each type they found. Were there any that they were unsure about?
Sort them out Use the headings of the given square to work out the only numbers (1 to 16) that could fit into the square.	Explore patterns, properties and relationships and propose a general statement involving numbers or shapes; identify examples for which the statement is true or false	**Before:** Ask the children to explain the meaning of the vocabulary used in the puzzle. **After:** Share results. Invite individuals to explain their thinking when they decided where to place the numbers.
Calculations page Practise the written addition and subtraction methods learned in class.	Use efficient written methods to add and subtract whole numbers	**Before:** Ask the children to remind you of possible pitfalls when using the various written methods. **After:** Check through answers together and troubleshoot difficulties.
Card trick Use the three-ring Venn diagram to sort the numbers found on a set of playing cards.	Identify pairs of factors of two-digit whole numbers and find common multiples (for example, for 6 and 9)	**Before:** Children will need a set of playing cards at home. If not, show them a pack in class and explain that the picture cards represent the following values: Ace (1), Jack (11), Queen (12) and King (13). **After:** Check that each of the numbers has been located in the correct ring(s). Discuss the advantages of using a diagram like this for recording certain kinds of information.
You're the teacher Mark a test paper with questions about money addition.	Use knowledge of place value and number facts to estimate and check calculations	**Before:** Perform a column addition on the board and stress the importance of lining up the decimal points. **After:** Go through the answers with the class.
B2		
Carl's chocolate chips Children test their knowledge of multiples, division and problem-solving strategies.	Represent a problem by identifying and recording the calculations needed to solve it; find possible solutions and confirm them in the context of the problem	**Before:** Explain to the children that they need to show how they solve this problem. **After:** Invite the children to explain their strategies.
Multiple sort Play a times-table game.	Recall quickly multiplication facts up to 10 × 10	**Before:** Explain the rules and tell the children that some numbers are in more than one times table. They must identify at least one of them. **After:** Invite the children to discuss the more difficult numbers. Do they need to relearn any times tables?
Reflect on that Complete a symmetrical pattern.	Complete patterns with up to two lines of symmetry; draw the position of a shape after a reflection or translation	**Before:** Ask the children to remind you how a shape or point may be reflected. **After:** Ask the children to swap their patterns with a partner and check the patterns.

BLOCK B

Securing number facts, understanding shape

Activity name	Learning objectives	Managing the homework
Flip it! Reflect shapes coordinate by coordinate.	Complete patterns with up to two lines of symmetry; draw the position of a shape after a reflection or translation	**Before:** Invite the children to tell you how to reflect solid shapes, coordinate by coordinate. **After:** Ask the children to swap their grids with a partner and check the accuracy of the reflections.
Thinking of a number Answer number puzzles involving halving and doubling.	Use knowledge of place value and addition and subtraction of two-digit numbers to derive sums and differences and doubles and halves of decimals (for example, 6.5 ± 2.7, half of 5.6, double 0.34)	**Before:** Practise doubling and halving two-digit numbers mentally. **After:** Discuss the techniques the children used to solve the puzzles.
Shape nets Identify the correct nets of 3D shapes.	Identify, visualise and describe properties of rectangles, triangles, regular polygons and 3D solids; use knowledge of properties to draw 2D shapes and identify and draw nets of 3D shapes	**Before:** Remind the class what a net of a 3D shape is. **After:** Ask the children to cut out the correctly identified nets and fold them to form the 3D shapes.
B3		
Number creatures Children are required to think creatively and use known number facts to develop number sentences.	Represent a problem by identifying and recording the calculations needed to solve it; find possible solutions and confirm them in the context of the problem	**Before:** Recall known number facts - doubles, table facts and number bonds. **After:** Invite the children to share some of their number sentences with the class.
The school barbecue Answer money questions related to a real-life situation (catering for a barbecue).	• Represent a problem by identifying and recording the calculations needed to solve it; find possible solutions and confirm them in the context of the problem • Use efficient written methods to add and subtract whole numbers and decimals with up to two places	**Before:** Discuss with the children the strategies they might use to answer these questions. **After:** Compare answers and invite some children to discuss their methods.
Target number game Play a target number game, using +, -, × and ÷.	Represent a problem by identifying and recording the calculations needed to solve it; find possible solutions and confirm them in the context of the problem	**Before:** Explain the rules and have a 'practice run' in class. **After:** Invite individuals to share their most inventive calculations.
Colour me odd or even? Decide what sort of numbers are generated when various operations are applied.	• Explore patterns, properties and relationships and propose a general statement involving numbers or shapes; identify examples for which the statement is true or false • Represent a problem by identifying and recording the calculations needed to solve it; find possible solutions and confirm them in the context of the problem	**Before:** Invite the children to share observations they made about calculating with odd and even numbers. **After:** Ask the children to check with a partner that they have the same odd and even answers as each other. Iron out difficulties.
Viewing times Round large numbers to the nearest 1000.	Use knowledge of rounding, place value and number facts to estimate and check calculations.	**Before:** Write a six-digit number on the board and round it up/down to the nearest 1000. **After:** Go through the answers with the class.
Drawing shapes Draw and name 2D shapes with a given number of right angles.	Identify, visualise and describe properties of rectangles, triangles and regular polygons; use knowledge of properties to draw 2D shapes	**Before:** Recap on how to use a protractor or angle measurer. **After:** Make a display of the children's drawings. Discuss solutions to problems encountered. Ask: *What would you do differently next time?*

Name	Date

Times-table challenge

- How fast can you complete each times-table grid?
- Write your time at the bottom.
- Now colour in all the square numbers.

×	2	3	4	5	6	7	8
2							
4							
8							
3							
6							
9							

Time: _____

×	3	4	5	6	7	8	9
4							
5							
9							
3							
7							
2							

Time: _____

×	4	5	6	7	8	9	10
2							
3							
4							
5							
6							
7							

Time: _____

×	6	5	7	8	9	3	4
8							
4							
5							
9							
7							
6							

Time: _____

Dear Helper

This homework should be timed. Your child's speed should improve with practice. It is not necessary for your child to complete all four grids at one sitting. It would be helpful to do some learning practice with your child after they complete each grid. This could take the form of you calling out quick-fire times-tables questions, such as: *What is 3 × 4?* or *How many 5s in 25?* It is not enough to be able to find the answer by chanting through the tables, because an instant response is required (though knowing the tables is a good starting point). If your child is confident with 10-times table facts, challenge them to try multiplying 11, 12 or 13 by 2, 3, 4, 5 and 6. Use an extra sheet for this purpose.

BLOCK B

Name   Date

BLOCK B

Sorting triangles

◖ Can you remember the definitions of different sorts of triangles?

◖ Look at the triangles below. Colour all the equilateral triangles blue, all the isosceles triangles red and all the scalene triangles green.

    ☐ You will need a ruler and a protractor.

◖ Write the definitions you used:

Equilateral _____

Isosceles _____

Scalene _____

◖ Can a scalene triangle also be a right-angled triangle? _____

Dear Helper

This is a sorting activity that uses criteria learned at school. There are three distinct kinds of triangle. You should encourage your child to think about triangles in terms of how long the sides are, how big the angles are, and where the lines of symmetry are. (A line of symmetry divides a shape into two halves that are mirror images of each other.) An equilateral triangle has three equal sides; an isosceles triangle has two equal sides; a scalene triangle has no equal sides. If your child finds this activity difficult, you may need to help them to measure the sides accurately. If they are confident in the activity, challenge them to look around your home for three examples of each type of triangle. Which type do you find most often? Which triangle is less often used in buildings?

Name	Date

Sort them out

■ Fill in this grid, using the numbers 1–16 only once each. Each number must follow the rules for the row and the column that it belongs to. The first number has been done for you.

1, 2, 3, 4, 5, 6, 7, 8, 9, 10, 11, 12, 13, 14, 15, 16

	even number	factor of 24	< 8	odd number
square number	16			
> 6				
multiple of 3				
< 12				

BLOCK B

Dear Helper

This puzzle helps your child to solve problems including factors, multiples and square numbers. It needs to be approached methodically, as several numbers might fit in more than one cell. Your child needs to find the cells that have only one possible answer, and work carefully from there. There are some obvious starting points – for example, 1 and 9 are the only square numbers in the list that are odd, and only one of them is less than 8. If your child has found this puzzle easy, challenge them to invent a similar puzzle using different sorting criteria. Can you solve it?

Name   Date

BLOCK B

Calculations page

◢ Work out these problems, using a written calculation method of your choice.

421 + 138	
271 + 496	
1143 − 110	
349 − 164	
721 − 348	
289 + 877	
3014 + 1896	

Dear Helper
Please remind your child that they must use a written calculation method. They can choose the best one from the methods they know. They may need help with remembering to 'carry' extra tens or hundreds across to the next column when adding, or with splitting up a tens or hundreds number when subtracting. As an extra challenge, ask your child to add up the answers to the first five calculations, then subtract the answer to the final one.

Name   Date

Card trick

🔲 You are going to carry out a data handling activity using the numbers on a set of playing cards.

🔲 Draw a large version of this Venn diagram on which to write your data.

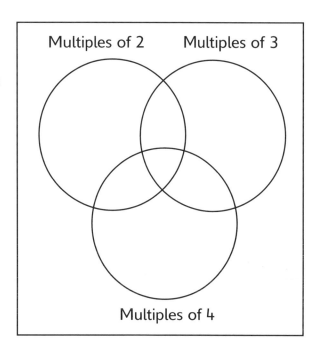

☐ Choose one of the four suits. Cards 2 to 10 will count at their face value. The ace will count as 1, the Jack as 11, the Queen as 12 and the King as 13.

☐ Select the cards at random and write the numbers 1–13, inclusive, in the correct section of the Venn diagram.

☐ The rings should contain the multiples of 2, 3 and 4. If a number meets two of the criteria, write it where the two rings overlap. If it meets three criteria, write it where the three rings overlap. If it does not meet any, write it in the box outside the rings.

☐ Now choose ten of the same cards at random and see if you can use a Venn diagram to sort them in a different way. Try odd and even numbers, or square numbers possibly.

🔲 Make another Venn diagram using three rings like the one in the box above. Label them 'rainy', 'cloudy' and 'sunny'. Talk about weather conditions in the last week. Place each day in the correct ring or rings. Why might some days appear in two or even all three of the rings?

Dear Helper
A set of playing cards will be needed in order to carry out this task. In this method of showing data, rings are used instead of axes or boxes. This version is called a Venn diagram. It is named after John Venn, a mathematician who taught at Cambridge University in the Victorian era. He used diagrams to help simplify relationships between groups of numbers. Provide your child with a suitable large circle to draw around, as it will speed up the recording process. Make sure the rings are always labelled carefully.

Name   Date

You're the teacher

 Here is a copy of Mike's test paper.

Mike Jones   12 May, 2009

1) £1.45 + £1.78 + £2.43 = £5.73

2) £2.99 + £4.28 + 68p = £7.97

3) £2.37 + £8.25 + £1.12 = £11.74

4) £7.70 + £7.07 + 70p = £21.77

5) 93p + £3.69 + £6.16 + 46p = £11.26

6) £16.72 + £56.88 + £31.99 = £104.60

7) £6.06 + £99.99 + 87p + £37.41 = £145.05

1. How many questions did Mike answer correctly?

2. What are the correct answers for the ones he got wrong?

Dear Helper

This activity helps your child to practise column addition. Make sure your child lines up the decimal points, keeps the place values correct, carries over any extra digits to the next place value, records them beneath the sum and remembers to add any extras to the next column. This is very likely the way you were taught at school!

Unit B2 📖 **Homework activity**

Name	Date

Carl's chocolate chips

◼ Carl had between 30 and 50 chocolate chips.

☐ He counted the chocolate chips in 4s. There were two left over.

☐ He counted them again in 5s. There was one left over.

◼ How many chocolate chips did Carl have? _____

Name _____ Date _____

Multiple sort

■ **This is a game for two to four players.**

☐ Carefully cut out the number cards below. Shuffle the cards and place them face down. Take turns to pick one card up.

☐ The first player to call out a times table and a multiplication fact that the number belongs to wins the card. For example: '81 is in the 9-times table, 9 × 9 is 81' or '72 is in the 8- (or 9-) times table, 8 × 9 = 72'.

☐ The player with the most cards at the end is the winner.

81	12	30	48	72
32	49	42	21	35
18	36	56	64	63
27	40	90	28	16

Dear Helper

This activity encourages your child to recall facts from the 6-, 7-, 8- and 9-times tables. It can, of course, be extended to include the other factors of the numbers on the cards. If your child is unsure, encourage them by reciting the appropriate tables together. However, this would be a sign that they needed to spend time learning the multiplication facts so that they could recall them easily.

Name   Date

Reflect on that

■ Complete the symmetrical pattern below by reflecting the shapes in all mirror lines.

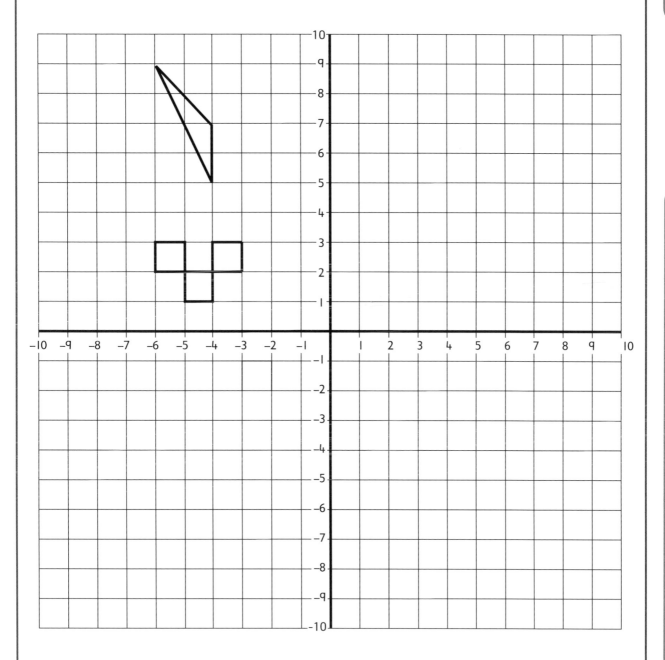

BLOCK B

Dear Helper

The important thing to remember with reflecting shapes is that they 'flip over' when reflected so it is sometimes necessary to count the number of squares from each point or corner as shown. Don't forget to reflect the reflection in order to complete a symmetrical pattern in all four quadrants. A further challenge might be to encourage your child to create their own pattern.

Name   Date

Flip it!

■ Reflect the shapes in both mirror lines.

  ▢ Remember to number each reflected point A1, B1, C1, A2, B2, C2 and so on.

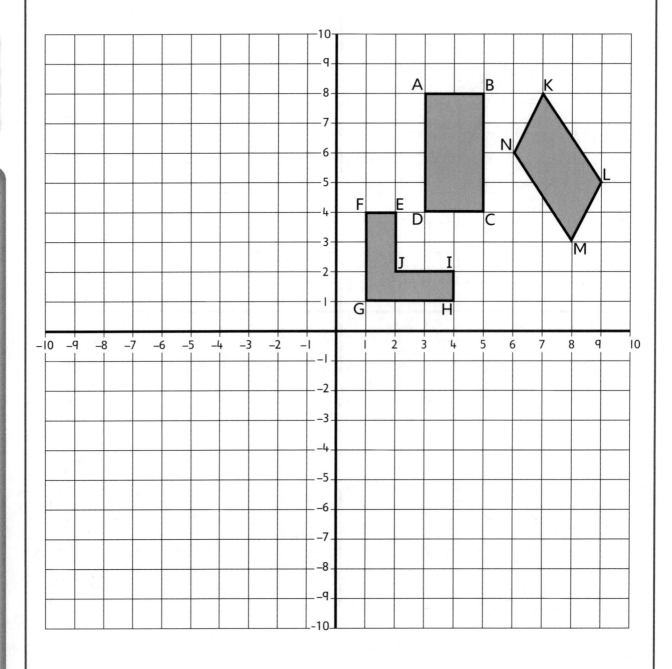

BLOCK B

Dear Helper
This exercise requires children to reflect each point separately and then join them up. To reflect a point your child needs to count the number of squares up to the mirror line and the same number away again on the other side of the mirror line. Each shape will invert or 'flip over' as it crosses the mirror line. A further challenge might be to draw a new set of axes on the back of this sheet and draw additional shapes to reflect.

Name	Date

Thinking of a number

◀ Answer these number puzzles set by Magical Misty.

1. I am thinking of a number: it is odd and if I halve it I get 7.5. What is my number?

2. I am thinking of a number: if I double it, then double it again, I will have 48. What is my number?

3. I am thinking of a number: it is a decimal number and if I halve it I'll be left with 3.7. What is my number?

4. I am thinking of a number: it is a decimal number and if I double it I will have 55. What is my number?

5. I am thinking of a number: the total of its digits is 13 and when I halve it I get 38. What is my number?

6. I am thinking of a number: it is a whole number; if I halve it, halve it again and halve it again, I'm left with 12.5. What is my number?

Dear Helper

This activity helps your child to use their knowledge of place value and addition and subtraction to halve and double decimals. Encourage your child to use their mental arithmetic strategies to answer these questions (only make notes if necessary). Remind them to read each question carefully, and then read through it again to be sure they know what they are being asked to do.

Name	Date

Shape nets

- Look at these 3D shapes.
- Next to each shape are two possible nets. However, only one of the nets will form that particular shape.
- Identify the correct net for each 3D shape. Mark it with a tick.

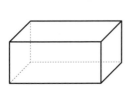  

 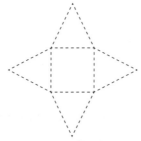 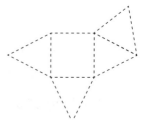

 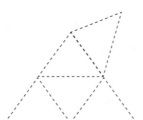 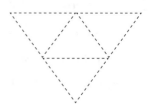

BLOCK B

Name	Date

Number creatures

🔳 Look at the number displayed on each of these creatures. In each box, write as many different number sentences as you can to make that number.

▫ An example has been done for you for the first number creature.

7 × 5

Dear Helper
This activity helps your child to think about all four number operations (+, −, ×, ÷) and be inventive about using them. Try to discourage your child from simply adding 1 or taking away 1. If your child is finding the activity difficult, use counters or coins to help them get a visual image of the numbers. If your child is confident with making number sentences, challenge them to attempt two-step operations – for example, making 35 by doubling 15 and then adding 5.

Name

Date

BLOCK B

The school barbecue

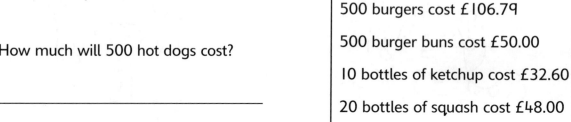

- The school PTA is organising a school barbecue.

- They need to calculate how much food to buy, how much it will cost, and how much to charge for each item to ensure they make a profit.

- They estimate that 500 people will attend.

- Use the information in the box to answer the questions below.

| 500 rolls cost £50.00 |
| 500 sausages cost £118.25 |
| 500 burgers cost £106.79 |
| 500 burger buns cost £50.00 |
| 10 bottles of ketchup cost £32.60 |
| 20 bottles of squash cost £48.00 |

1. How much will 500 hot dogs cost?

_____

2. How much will 500 burgers in buns cost?

_____

3. How much will 500 burgers in buns and 500 hot dogs cost altogether?

_____

4. Add on the cost of the squash and ketchup. What is the grand total spent?

_____

5. If they charge each person £3.00, they will take £1500. How much profit will be made?

_____

Dear Helper

Please encourage your child to read the questions carefully and to add the numbers in pairs as asked. Encourage your child to use a written method of subtraction. Please do not use a calculator. If your child is struggling, it might help to convert the word problem into a calculation (some children have difficulty recognising which operation to use: ×, ÷, – or +). Write the calculations beside the written questions. Once your child is confident with the task, challenge them to plan their own event and price each item. If available, the data can be entered into a spreadsheet program such as Microsoft Excel, which allows you to change unit costs and recalculate.

Name	Date

Target number game

◼ **This is a game for two to four players.**

☐ Carefully cut out the number cards below. Turn them face up.

☐ Use any of the numbers once and any operation to make the target numbers shown in the table.

☐ Record the calculation you used.

☐ Speed is important because the first person to make their target number gets a point. Two points may be awarded for a more complex calculation using all four operations.

Player 1 TARGET	Calculation	Player 2 TARGET	Calculation
11		11	
5		5	
77		77	
18		18	
20		20	
52		52	

✂

2	6	7	4	12	21

Dear Helper
Remind your child that 'all four operations' means +, −, ÷ and ×. They may use any or all of them in one calculation. Children who find multiplication and division difficult could see how many of the numbers can be made simply by adding and subtracting. Alternatively, the person who gets closest to the given numbers could be the winner, using whichever operations they feel confident with. A further challenge might be to make a new set of number cards using more challenging numbers such as 17 and 41, but keeping the same target numbers.

Colour me odd or even?

■ Colour all the sections that give an even answer one colour and the sections that give an odd number a second colour.

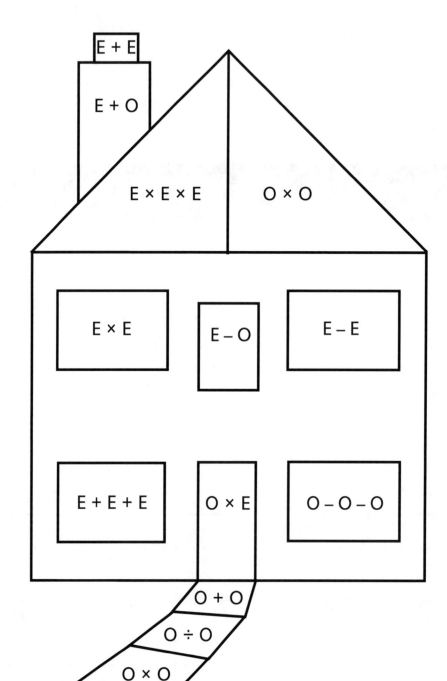

Colour key:

☐ = Odd (O)
☐ = Even (E)

Dear Helper
Certain patterns emerge when calculating with odd and even numbers. If your child is in any doubt, try a couple of examples using numbers to help you decide whether the answer will be odd or even. Challenge your child to create their own picture and odd and even questions.

BLOCK B

Name   Date

Viewing times

◼ These are the TV viewing figures for a week.

◼ Round them to the nearest 1000.

Programme	Viewers	Rounded to the nearest 1000
Londoners	178,473	
Sing to Win	374,294	
Hospital Drama	472,672	
Football Live	835,333	
The Constabulary	472,567	
All Aboard!	628,342	
Daily News	934,681	
Cooking Today	462,489	
School Quiz Challenge	814,557	
Star Quality	992,103	

◼ Roughly how many viewers watched the following programmes?
Answer to the nearest 1000.

1. Londoners and Hospital Drama _____

2. The Constabulary and Star Quality _____

3. Daily News and Football Live _____

4. School Quiz Challenge and All Aboard! _____

5. Sing to Win and Cooking Today _____

Dear Helper
This activity helps your child to round large numbers and use rounding to estimate. Estimating is
a good skill to use in maths. When doing the additions, encourage your child to estimate first, then
calculate, and then to check their answers. Look for some large numbers in newspapers and do the same
exercise. Attendances at football matches are a good example. Ask, for example: *Roughly how many
people attended the United match and the Arsenal match altogether?*

Name   Date

BLOCK B

Drawing shapes

◼ You will need a ruler for this activity. Your challenge is to follow the instructions to draw these shapes. Write the names of the shapes you have drawn underneath.

1. A four-sided shape with no right angles.

This is a —————————.

2. A three-sided shape with one right angle.

This is a —————————.

3. A five-sided shape with one right angle.

This is a —————————.

4. A six-sided shape with three right angles.

This is a —————————.

5. A seven-sided shape with four right angles.

This is a —————————.

6. A six-sided shape with all angles and sides the same size.

This is a —————————.

Dear Helper
This activity helps your child to Identify, visualise and describe properties of rectangles, triangles and regular polygons. They may need help with measuring and drawing some of the angles. If they want to be super-accurate, they can use a protractor. It will help your child if they can picture the shape they want to draw in their mind first. They can practise on the back of this sheet before drawing their shapes in the boxes. When naming the shapes, remind them that shapes with all sides equal and all angles equal are 'regular' polygons, all others are 'irregular'.

Handling data and measures

Activity name	Learning objectives	Managing the homework
C1		
Collecting and representing data Set a question, then collect data to answer it. Collect the information on a tally chart and draw the most suitable type of graph to represent the data.	• Answer a set of related questions by collecting, selecting and organising relevant data; draw conclusions, using ICT to present features, and identify further questions to ask • Construct frequency tables, pictograms and bar and line graphs to represent the frequencies of events and changes over time	**Before:** Make a class list of all the different suggestions the children can make about data that could be collected and represented as a graph. **After:** Ask some children to present their findings to the rest of the class. Make a class display.
Weights and measures Look in cupboards at home or go shopping to find out what measures items are generally sold in. Find out if there any standard quantities.	Read, choose, use and record standard metric units to estimate and measure length, weight and capacity to a suitable degree of accuracy (for example, the nearest centimetre)	**Before:** Emphasise the permission issue and the safety warning regarding cleaning materials. **After:** Invite the children to make generalisations. Display their findings.
Ordering masses Order weights of food packages by converting all into decimals of kg from g (for example, 500g = 0.5kg).	Read, choose, use and record standard metric units to estimate and measure length, weight and capacity to a suitable degree of accuracy (for example, the nearest centimetre); convert larger to smaller units using decimals to one place (for example, change 2.6kg to 2600g)	**Before:** Stress the health and safety implications of this activity and the importance of asking for adult permission. **After:** Amalgamate some of the homework results into a class weights-and-measures number line.
How much? Solve some word problems.	Read, choose, use and record standard metric units to estimate and measure length, weight and capacity to a suitable degree of accuracy (for example, the nearest centimetre); convert larger to smaller units using decimals to one place (for example, change 2.6kg to 2600g)	**Before:** Ask the children to remind you of the order of working through word problems. **After:** Discuss the methods used.
C2		
Every graph tells a story Look at a line graph, label its axes and tell the graph's story.	• Plan and pursue an enquiry; present evidence by collecting, organising and interpreting information; suggest extensions to the enquiry • Construct line graphs to represent the frequencies of events and changes over time	**Before:** Discuss with the children what the line graph could mean and what the x and y axes represent. **After:** Make a display of suggestions for this graph story.
That's impossible! Make judgements on statements of probability.	Describe the occurrence of familiar events using the language of chance or likelihood	**Before:** Discuss the words 'certain', 'unlikely', 'likely' and 'impossible'. **After:** Share the answers given by the class. Discuss the meaning of 'certain' and 'impossible' as these may throw up some interesting answers.
How long? Estimate then measure the lengths of everyday items to the nearest centimetre.	Read, choose, use and record standard metric units to estimate and measure length to a suitable degree of accuracy (for example, the nearest centimetre)	**Before:** Ensure that everyone has a ruler for this activity. **After:** Compare answers between measurements of the same object, such as the length of a DVD cover.
Problems with peas, pins, paper and pennies! Find solutions to problems by multiplying and dividing by 100 and 1000.	Interpret a reading that lies between two unnumbered divisions on a scale	**Before:** Ask the class how they would measure the thickness of one piece of paper. Discuss solutions offered. **After:** Go through the answers. Did everyone use the multiplying and dividing technique?

Handling data and measures

Activity name	Learning objectives	Managing the homework
C3		
Comparing data Answer questions from two line graphs displayed together on the same axes.	Answer a set of related questions by collecting, selecting and organising relevant data; draw conclusions, using ICT to present features, and identify further questions to ask	**Before:** Ask the children to study the questions and remind them of vocabulary such as 'difference', 'line graph' and 'bar line graph'. **After:** Invite some children to share further questions that could have been asked about this graph, for others to answer.
Missing data Add missing information to graphs and answer questions relating to them.	● Construct bar and line graphs to represent the frequencies of events and changes over time ● Answer a set of related questions by organising relevant data	**Before:** Look at the graphs and point out the information that is shown in them. **After:** Invite some children to share further questions that could have been asked about the graphs, for others to answer.
Fruit facts Draw a comparative bar graph and interpret it to find information.	● Construct bar graphs to represent the frequencies of events ● Answer a set of related questions by organising relevant data	**Before:** Ask the children to remind you how to draw a comparative bar chart and how to find the median of a set of data. **After:** Discuss any difficulties.
Sort it! Use a Carroll diagram to sort information and answer questions.	Answer a set of related questions by collecting, selecting and organising relevant data; draw conclusions, using ICT to present features, and identify further questions to ask	**Before:** Invite the children to tell you how a Carroll diagram is used. **After:** Share the results of children's own diagrams. Make a class display.

Name   Date

Collecting and representing data

- Collect data about something that interests you.
- Set yourself a question to answer – for example, "What is the most popular type of vehicle that passes my house in an hour?" or "How many of the different types of minibeasts can I find in one area of the garden?"
- Collect the information in a tally chart (see below), then decide on the best type of graph to represent your information.
- Draw the graph on a separate sheet of paper. Don't forget to label the axes and give the graph a title.
- Can you use the graph to answer your question?

The question I want to investigate:

_____

_____

Tally chart (use as much of this as you need):

My results: I found out that...

_____

_____

Dear Helper

This activity will help your child to collect data and draw a graph in order to answer a question. Any question along the lines of 'How many...', 'How high...', 'Which is the most popular...?' will be appropriate. The investigation is in two parts: collecting data and recording it in a tally chart, then drawing a graph. Please remind your child that a line graph is the best way to show measurable data that changes with time, such as temperature; a bar line graph is best for comparing different items, such as types of minibeasts or cars. If your child finds the concepts of graphs difficult, choose only a small number of comparisons and number the vertical axis in ones. A more challenging graph might be one where there is a very high number of items to be counted, where the vertical axis would need to be labelled as one square for every 5 or 10, thus requiring estimation.

Name	Date

Weights and measures

- ◼ With an adult, look in your store cupboards at home, or accompany an adult when they go shopping.
- ◼ Find out what weights and measures packaged items are generally sold in.
- ◼ You might like to use the shopping list below, or make up a list of your own. (WARNING: Avoid cleaning materials or other products that might be dangerous.)
- ◼ In the space at the bottom of this sheet, write about what you have found.
- ◼ Are there any standard quantities for items? For example, is milk always sold in the same quantity (or multiples of that quantity)?

My research shopping list	Weights and measures
jam	
washing powder	
milk	
fizzy drink	
flour	
sugar	
rice	
soup	
tinned tomatoes	
baked beans	

What I found out:

_____

_____

_____

_____

Dear Helper

Most items we buy are available in certain standard amounts, and in this activity, your child is finding out about how weights and measures are standardised. You can help by letting your child look in your food cupboards and pointing out similarities to them – for example, tins are generally in one of three standard sizes. Encourage your child to look for general trends in the weights and measures they see. Challenge them to find out how many servings each container holds. They could also work out how many of each item they would need to buy to feed 50 people.

Name	Date

Ordering masses

◀ WARNING! Ask permission at home before you do this activity, and make sure an adult is watching you before you handle any containers. Don't touch cleaning materials or other chemicals. Remember to put everything away neatly after you have finished.

◀ Find eight different jars and packets in your store cupboards that are weighed in grams or kilograms. Put them in order of increasing mass (the lightest first). To do this, you will have to convert them all into the same unit of measurement: kilograms (kg). For example, 500g = 0.5kg. Record the masses by drawing and labelling them in this grid.

1	5
2	6
3	7
4	8

Dear Helper

This activity involves looking at different masses (weights) and converting them to a common unit (kilograms, kg). Having a common unit makes the numbers easier to order. If your child is struggling, please do not weigh the items, since the jars, bottles and tins are labelled with the mass of the contents alone. Please do not confuse your child by converting into pounds and ounces! Encourage your child to convert all the masses to grams and then order the items physically before recording them on the grid. As a further challenge, ask your child to estimate the masses of some items in grams and then convert them to kg. Even small masses can be estimated and recorded in this way (for example, 25g = 0.025kg).

Name   Date

How much?

◾ Solve the following problems.

1. My cat weighs 3.1kg and my dog weighs 5900g. How much is their combined mass?

2. Mrs Jones needs 6.8m of fabric for curtains and a further 320cm of the same material for cushions. How much fabric should she buy?

3. On a round trip to work, Mum drives 8km to drop Dan at his friend's house and pick up my friend Ellie. She then takes Ellie and me 5km to school. Finally she drives a further 8420m to her office. How far does she drive to work each day? She repeats the journey on the way home. How far does she drive each day? How far does she drive in a five-day school week?

4. My dad filled his car up at the petrol station. He bought 37 litres of fuel. The next day, he found that the tank was nearly empty because my brother had borrowed the car. Dad was not pleased about having to buy another 32,000ml of fuel. How much fuel had Dad bought in two days? How many litres of fuel had my brother used up?

Dear Helper
This activity helps your child to remember equivalent measures, such as the number of metres in a kilometre. These amounts can be quite difficult to remember, but they are important in real life. You can help your child by doing conversions as they occur in your daily life – for example, when you are shopping or buying petrol. As a challenge, think of some real-life examples of similar problems, and ask your child to write them on the back of this sheet and solve them. For example: *Six bags of crisps cost £1.14. Each bag contains 28g of crisps. What is the total mass of the six bags? How much does one bag cost?*

PHOTOCOPIABLE ◾◾SCHOLASTIC

BLOCK C

Name   Date

Every graph tells a story

- Look at the line graph below. What story do you think it is telling?
- Give the graph a title and label the axes.
- Write the story. For example: 'At _____ o'clock _____ happened.'

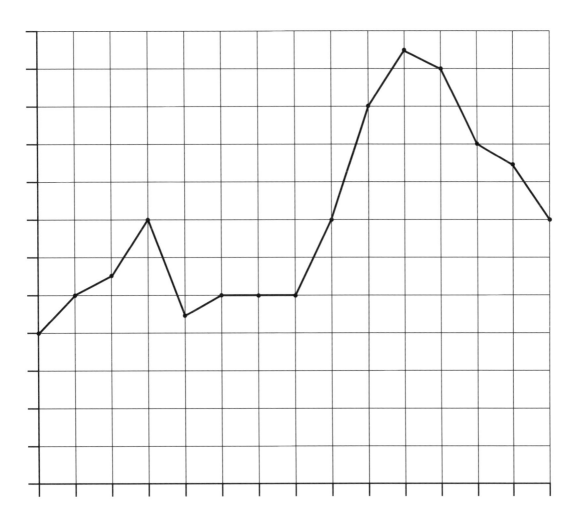

Dear Helper
This graph gives your child an opportunity to think imaginatively. There are no 'right' or 'wrong' answers. Encourage your child to be inventive.

BLOCK C

Name   Date

That's impossible!

- Describe the occurrence of familiar events using the language of chance or likelihood.
- Read the following statements and decide whether each is impossible, unlikely, likely or certain.
- Draw a line from each statement to one of the four word boxes.

1. It will snow on Christmas Day in London.

2. The sun will rise tomorrow.

3. Gromit the dog will be the next president of the USA.

4. I will go to school next Monday morning.

5. The England football team will win the next World Cup.

6. The Atlantic Ocean will turn into tomato soup by teatime.

7. The news will be on TV tonight.

8. I will become an international pop star and have five number ones.

9. My favourite soft toy will come to life and become my personal servant.

| Impossible |
| Unlikely |
| Likely |
| Certain |

Dear Helper

This activity helps your child to using the vocabulary of chance or likelihood. Your child might read the statements and jump to immediate conclusions. Encourage them to read them carefully and consider their thoughts – some are not as clear-cut as they seem. Challenge your child to make up some statements of their own and record them on the back of this sheet.

PHOTOCOPIABLE

BLOCK C

Name   Date

How long?

◾ You will need a ruler for this activity.

◾ Find examples of the everyday household items listed in the table below.

◾ Estimate the length of each item in centimetres.

◾ Now measure them to the nearest centimetre.

Item	Estimated length (cm)	Measured length (cm)
A magazine		
A DVD case		
A teaspoon		
A paperback book		
A radiator		
Your bed		
A door		
A pencil		
A pair of trousers		

◾ How close were your estimates to the actual answer?

Dear Helper

This activity helps your child to estimate and measure length to a suitable degree of accuracy. If you have a tape measure, you could ask your child to estimate and measure the length of larger objects or distances. You and your child should also see a steep learning curve of accuracy in their estimates. The more they estimate and measure, the better they should get!

BLOCK C

Name   Date

Problems with peas, pins, paper and pennies!

- Ollie has been set a challenge by his friend Sarinda.

- Sarinda has said she will give Ollie his weight in chocolate if he can answer these questions:

  - ☐ How heavy is one pea?

  - ☐ How heavy is one pin?

  - ☐ How heavy is one penny?

  - ☐ How thick is one piece of paper?

- Ollie knows he can win the challenge and win the chocolate.

  - ☐ How can he do this?

  - ☐ What equipment does he need?

  - ☐ How could dividing by 100 or 1000 help find the answers?

Dear Helper

This activity helps your child to read scales accurately. The problem appears to be difficult but encourage your child to think about it and explore the ideas they may have. The answer is to measure the weight of 100 peas and divide the answer by 100, or measure the height of a pile of 50 sheets of paper and divide by 50. If you have the equipment at home you could try it.

Name	Date

Comparing data

- Look at these two line graphs. They show the temperatures in London and Athens over one 12-hour period in summer.
- Use the graphs to answer the questions below.
- Write your answers to questions 4 and 5 on the back of this sheet.

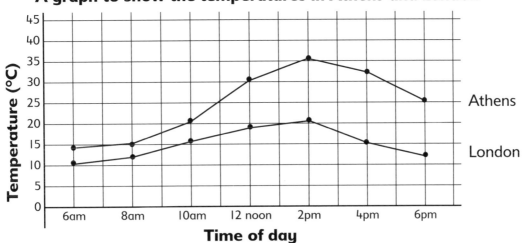

A graph to show the temperatures in Athens and London

1. What is the difference between the highest temperatures shown in Athens and London?

2. What is the difference between the highest and lowest temperatures in London?

3. What is the temperature in each city at 5:00pm?

4. Why is this information displayed as a line graph, not a bar chart or a bar line graph?

5. Give two examples of situations where a bar line graph would be appropriate, and two where a line graph should be used.

BLOCK C

Dear Helper
A line graph is used to show how something measurable (such as a person's temperature) changes over a period of time. A bar chart or a bar line graph is used to compare numbers of separate things, such as cars or different colour eyes. To help your child understand this, it may be helpful to explain that temperature never goes away: it may rise and fall, but it is always there and can be measured at all times. If your child finds reading the scale difficult, you can help them by dividing the space between values with four small lines or divisions to enable them to work out the temperature by counting on in ones. Challenge your child to write some more questions for you to answer, using the graphs.

Name _____ Date _____

Missing data

■ Complete these graphs from the information provided, then answer the questions below.

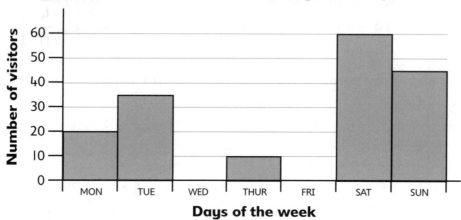

Bar graph to show the number of daily visitors to a website

1. There were 35 visitors on Wednesday. Draw the bar to show this.

2. There were 42 visitors on Friday. Show this information on the graph.

3. What was the total number of visitors to the website that week? _____

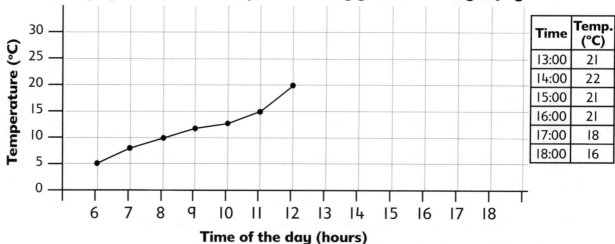

Line graph to show the temperature in my garden on a day in July

Time	Temp. (°C)
13:00	21
14:00	22
15:00	21
16:00	21
17:00	18
18:00	16

4. Complete the graph by adding the data shown in the table (see above right).

5. What was the median temperature for the day (6:00–18:00)? _____

Dear Helper

This activity will help your child to display data on graphs, and to interpret graphs. Encourage your child to look at the scale carefully, especially when recording a value between two marked points on the scale. The median is the middle value when the data are arranged in ascending order. If your child gets stuck, go through the information provided with them step by step.

Name	Date

Fruit facts

▰ A survey asked 100 Year 5 children (50 girls and 50 boys) which fruit they would choose to eat at break time. The table shown here displays the results.

▰ Draw a comparative bar graph below to show these results.

	Boys	Girls
bananas	6	12
pears	9	8
apples	0	4
satsumas	18	11
grapes	17	15

Bar graph to show _____

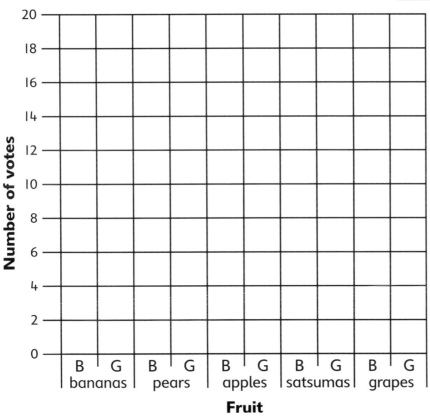

Key:

☐ Boys (B)

☐ Girls (G)

1. How many more boys than girls voted for satsumas? _____

2. What was the total number of votes for each fruit?_____

_____

3. Which was the most popular fruit overall? _____

4. Which was the least popular? _____

BLOCK C

Dear Helper
A comparative bar chart shows two bars in each column, coloured differently and given a key. This allows two sets of results to be compared directly. Encourage your child to understand the difference between finding the total number of votes (both boys and girls) and comparing the two sets of votes. If your child gets stuck, encourage them to go back to the original data and work step by step.

Name   Date

Sort it!

🔲 Use the information in this Carroll diagram to answer the questions below.

	Trousers that are jeans	Trousers that are not jeans
Blue	67	54
Not blue	37	48

1. How many pairs of trousers are blue? _____

2. How many are not blue? _____

3. How many more jeans are there than other kinds of trousers? _____

4. How many pairs of trousers are there altogether? _____

🔲 Think of some items that you could sort using a Carroll diagram. You could use colours, foods, animals or anything else you like.

🔲 Use the diagram below to sort the information you have collected.

🔲 Write some questions to go with your diagram, on the back of this sheet.

Dear Helper
This activity helps your child to use Carroll diagrams. A Carroll diagram sorts related items into groups. The numbers in the diagram above show how many pairs of trousers belong under each pair of headings. If your child finds it difficult to think of headings for their own diagram, suggest ideas such as 'Girl bands, boy bands, bands with fewer than four people, bands with four or more people'. Then they can fill in the names of bands that fit the given categories. Challenge your child to think of a diagram using numbers.

Calculating, measuring and understanding shape

Activity name	Learning objectives	Managing the homework
D1		
24 hours Children create a 24-hour map of what they might be doing at given times.	Read timetables and time using 24-hour clock notation	**Before:** Ask the children to remind you of times of the day in the 24-hour clock system. **After:** Display the results of the children's investigations.
Telling the time Collect examples of places around the home or town that use 24-hour digital notation and others that use the 12-hour am and pm system.	Read timetables and time using 24-hour clock notation	**Before:** Discuss places that need to display times. **After:** Share the class findings. Discuss why the system used might have been chosen.
Finding areas Find the area of given shapes, converting to the equivalent units of measure where necessary.	Use the formula for the area of a rectangle to calculate the rectangle's area	**Before:** Remind the children of the difficulties involved in mixed-unit calculations. **After:** Invite some of the children to describe how they found the area of the shapes that were not rectangles.
Living space Children draw a rough plan of a room in their house and find the area by dividing it into rectangles.	Use the formula for the area of a rectangle to calculate the rectangle's area	**Before:** Advise the children that they may have to round some of their measurements. Revise how to do this. **After:** Discuss any difficulties the children had.
D2		
Looking at lines Children are asked to find parallel and perpendicular lines in their homes.	Recognise parallel and perpendicular lines in grids and shapes	**Before:** Ask the children to remind you of the definitions of 'parallel' and 'perpendicular'. **After:** Invite the children to share their observations. Were there many examples where there were both parallel and perpendicular lines?
Missing angles Calculate the missing angle in a set of triangles.	Use efficient written methods to add and subtract whole numbers with up to two places	**Before:** Remind the children that the angles within a triangle always add up to 180°. **After:** Ask the children to explain how they answered the questions. Did they add the two given angles and subtract the answer from 180?
All at sea! Solve word problems that give practice in HTU × U multiplications.	Refine and use efficient written methods to multiply and divide HTU × U, TU × TU, U.t × U and HTU ÷ U	**Before:** Go through an HTU × U calculation on the board. Stress the importance of reading the questions carefully. **After:** Go through the answers. Were the children able to establish which calculations they were being asked to do?
Acute, obtuse or right? Identify acute, obtuse or right angles in an array of triangles.	Estimate and measure acute and obtuse angles using an angle measurer or protractor to a suitable degree of accuracy	**Before:** Remind the class of the definitions of acute, obtuse and right angles. **After:** Check that everyone is secure with this concept.

Calculating, measuring and understanding shape

Activity name	Learning objectives	Managing the homework
D3		
More times Practise long multiplication including decimals.	Refine and use efficient written methods to multiply HTU × U, TU × TU, and U.t × U	**Before:** Invite the children to tell you some rules for long multiplication and possible errors to avoid. **After**: Share answers and spot problems.
Translate and reflect Create a simple coordinate picture, then translate it and reflect it.	Complete patterns with up to two lines of symmetry; draw the position of a shape after a reflection or translation	**Before:** Ask the children to explain to you how to translate and reflect a coordinate. Tell them they will need to explain to their helpers at home! **After:** Compare and check the patterns created.
Activities diary Keep a time diary for given activities and calculate time spent doing these things in a day.	Read timetables and time using 24-hour clock notation; use a calendar to calculate time intervals	**Before:** Discuss the activities that the children do in a day. Ask them to estimate how many hours they spend in bed in a week. **After:** Compare the children's findings and use them as a basis for a display.
X marks the spot! Read and plot the coordinates of landmarks shown on a pirate map.	Read and plot coordinates in the first quadrant	**Before:** Remind the children of the conventions of reading coordinates on a grid. **After:** Go over the answers with the class. Did everyone go along the x axis first when reading and plotting the coordinates? Share the children's added landmarks.

Name	Date

24 hours

◼ Use the circle below to keep a diary of your activities for a day at the weekend.

☐ You could divide the hours into 30 minutes to be more accurate.

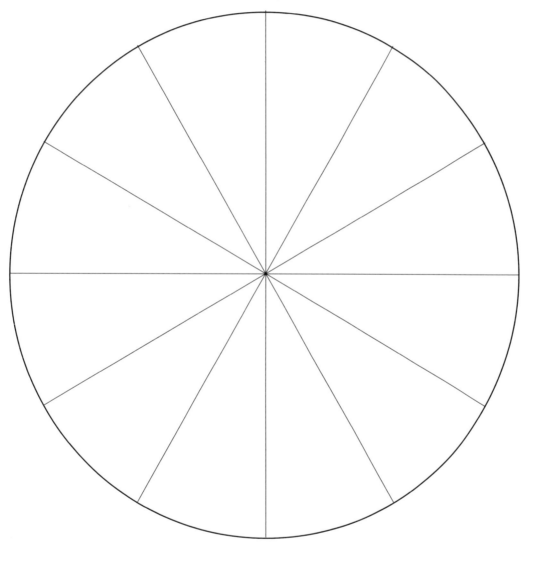

00:00
midnight

BLOCK D

Dear Helper

This activity will help your child to learn the 24-hour digital system. Please encourage your child to use the 24-hour clock when thinking about times. Perhaps you could remind them of this when saying the time in the afternoon or evening: instead of saying *It is 7:00* in the evening, you could say *It is 19:00*. If your child finds the 24-hour clock difficult, remind them that a 24-hour day is two sets of 12 hours, the first up to 12 noon and the second from noon until midnight. You might help them by drawing them these two 12-hour clocks side by side. Challenge your child by asking them to be more precise, giving their activity times in hours and minutes.

Name   Date

Telling the time

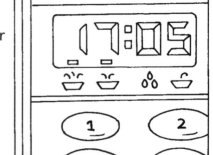

- Look around your home and town to find examples of some places that use the 24-hour system for telling the time and other places that use the 12-hour system. You might look at newspapers, timetables, clocks and shops.

- Record these places in the table below.

- Can you suggest a reason why that particular system of time-telling was chosen?

Place	12-hour or 24-hour system?	Why?

BLOCK D

Name   Date

Finding areas

◼ Find the area of these shapes. Look carefully at the units of measurement: you will need to convert some of them.

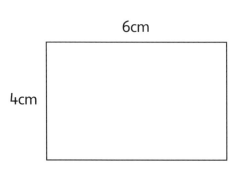

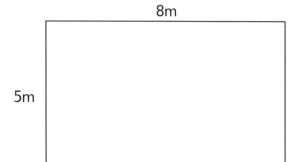

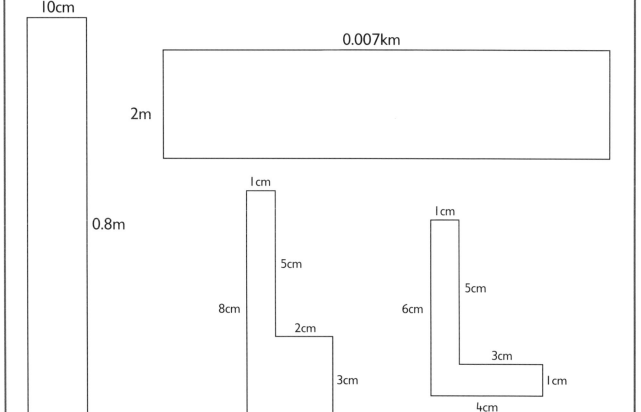

BLOCK D

Dear Helper

The area of a square or rectangle can be found by multiplying its length and its breadth (width), but this is only possible if the two measurements are in the same unit of measure (such as cm or m). If they are not, then one value must be changed by multiplying or dividing so that they are both in a common unit. It will help if your child remembers that there are 100cm in a metre and 1000m in a kilometre. If necessary, help your child to see that a composite shape such as an 'L' shape can be divided up into two or more rectangles; they can find the area of each rectangle, then add the areas together. Challenge your child to create a shape made up of rectangles and squares, then calculate the area.

Name	Date

Living space

- Choose a room in your house. Draw a rough plan of its shape in the space below. Leave some space under the plan for writing.

- Divide the shape you have drawn into squares or rectangles. Measure the length and breadth of each rectangle and mark these on your plan. It may be helpful to round the numbers to the nearest 10cm for easier multiplication.

- Now use the length × breadth formula to find the area of each rectangle. Mark the area of each section on your plan. Use these to calculate the total floor area of your room. Attempt the calculation without a calculator, and show your working here. You can then check your answer with a calculator!

Dear Helper

Your help will be essential with this exercise. Your child may find the plan of a room difficult to visualise, and you can help by indicating one wall at a time and pointing out any variations (such as alcoves). Look at the plan and help your child to divide it up into rectangles of various sizes. Remind them that the formula for finding area only applies to squares and rectangles. Help your child to measure one section at a time and label its length and breadth on the plan. Apply the formula to find the area of each section, then add these areas together to find the total floor area of the room. Challenge your child to draw a ground plan of one floor of your home, then calculate the approximate area.

PHOTOCOPIABLE ◼SCHOLASTIC

Name   Date

Looking at lines

- Look around your home (including the garden if you have one) for examples of parallel or perpendicular lines.

- Describe them in this table.

Type of lines	Example

Dear Helper

First establish with your child the difference between perpendicular lines (a pair of lines at right angles to each other) and parallel lines (a pair of lines that are equally spaced apart and will never meet or cross). Then look carefully around your home. Buildings have to be designed with perpendicular and parallel lines for stability. As a further challenge, ask your child to look for perpendicular lines that do not extend from a straight line but from a curved surface (for example, strings in a tennis racquet).

Name   Date

Missing angles

- The angles inside a triangle always add up to 180 degrees.
- Use this information to work out the missing angles in these triangles.

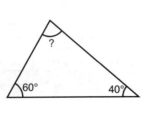

1 _____

2 _____

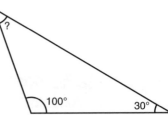

3 _____

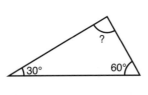

4 _____

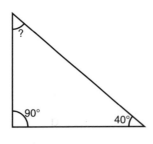

5 _____

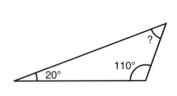

6 _____

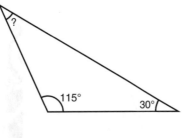

7 _____

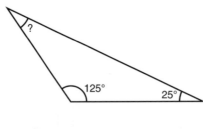

8 _____

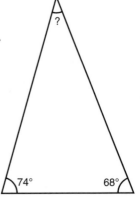

9 _____

10 _____

Dear Helper
This activity helps your child to practise adding and subtracting whole numbers. A quick method of calculating these is to add the two given angles then subtract the answer from 180. You can point this out to your child if they are struggling. As an extension activity, they could measure the angles in the triangles with a protractor or angle measurer to check their answers.

Name   Date

All at sea!

Captain Jack is loading his ship up with supplies for a long voyage. He needs to know how many items he is taking. However, he is not very good at maths! Help him by answering these questions.

1. Captain Jack wants to take 350 nails for each of his three masts. How many nails does he need to bring?

2. There are eight crew members. Each can bring 256 of their favourite biscuits. How many biscuits can be loaded on board?

3. Six barrels of apples, each containing 425 apples, are brought below deck. How many apples are there in total?

4. Each of the eight crew, plus Captain Jack, is allowed 512 rations of their favourite tipple – prune juice. How many rations of prune juice do they bring to drink?

5. There are seven cannonball racks, each holding 156 cannonballs. How many cannonballs are there in total?

6. The crew take five parrots and 673 packets of bird seed for each parrot. How many packets of bird seed are packed for the voyage?

7. Captain Jack has three wooden legs (two are spares!). They are all riddled with woodworm: each wooden leg has got 896 woodworms in it. How many woodworms are there altogether?

BLOCK D

Dear Helper

This activity helps your child to choose efficient written methods for multiplying and dividing. Word problems need careful reading so your child is able to work out which calculations they need to do. They need to sort out the useful information and disregard the rest. The general rule is to read the question, decide on the necessary calculation, estimate an answer, calculate and then check the answer.

Name _____   Date _____

Acute, obtuse or right?

An acute angle is less than 90 degrees.	An obtuse angle is more than 90 degrees, but less than 180 degrees.	A right angle is exactly 90 degrees.
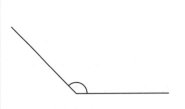	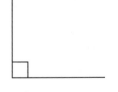	

◼ Label each of these angles either acute, obtuse or a right angle.

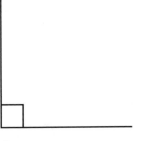

1 _____

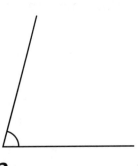

2 _____

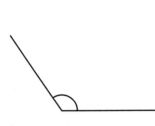

3 _____

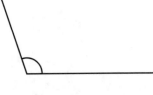

4 _____

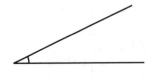

5 _____

6 _____

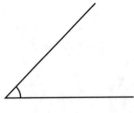

7 _____

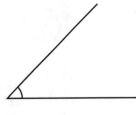

8 _____

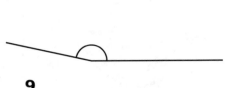

9 _____

BLOCK D

PHOTOCOPIABLE ■SCHOLASTIC

Name	Date

More times

◼ Use the multiplication methods you have learned to solve these written multiplication problems.

H T U	H T U	H T U
1 4 6	2 8 1	2 0 7
× 1 3	× 1 5	× 2 6

H T U	H T U	H T U
3 1 8	3 4 2	3 1 8
× 1 4	× 1 5	× 2 3

H T U . t h	H T U . t h	H T U . t h	H T U . t h
3 9 . 2 1	1 4 2 . 6 3	3 5 . 3 9	1 2 7 . 2 7
× 1 5	× 1 2	× 2 1	× 1 6

Dear Helper
This activity gives your child practice in long multiplication – that is, written multiplication by a number with more than one digit. The difficulty with the transition from simpler multiplications to long multiplication is the multiplication by the second digit (the tens in this case). If your child is having difficulty, you may need to remind them that if they are multiplying by a tens number, they need to move the answers up the place value line and write a zero in the units column to 'hold' the place value. Please allow your child to show you their method. Please don't teach them a new method. Challenge your child to increase the multiple of each question by 200 (for example, 342 × 15 becomes 342 × 215). Ask: *What will you have to do to multiply by 'hundreds'? How many place values will you have to hold?*

BLOCK D

Name   Date

Translate and reflect

- Use the coordinates below to create a simple picture.
- Translate it according to the formula $(x - 8, y)$ and then reflect the new image in the horizontal mirror line (x axis).

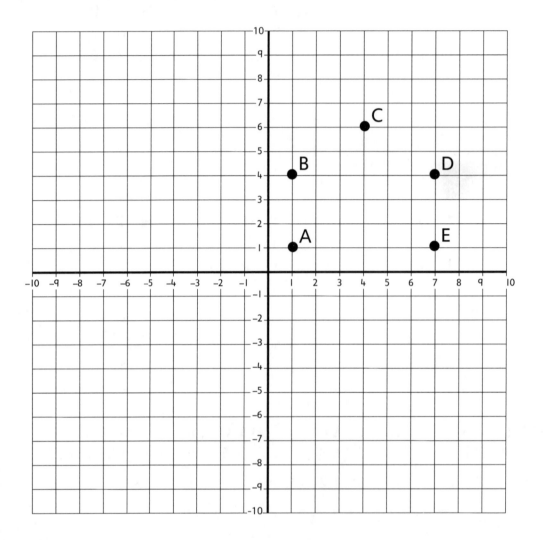

- Join all the points.
- Use the back of this sheet to calculate the coordinates of the new translated and reflected shape.

Dear Helper
Your child needs to be reminded that a translation will move points or shapes along, while reflections will invert them on the opposite side of the mirror line. To translate a shape, the coordinates (x, y) have a number added or subtracted, so a coordinate $(2, 4)$, when a formula such as $(x - 6, y - 4)$ is applied, would become $(-4, 0)$. If your child finds the translation formula difficult, help them by writing out the coordinates and then applying the formula together (ie take 8 away from the x coordinate but leave the y coordinate as it is). This will give you the new coordinates for the translated shape. Children can use the axis as a number line to help them calculate negative numbers when drawing the reflection. Challenge your child to create their own coordinates and formula to translate and reflect shapes.

Name	Date

Activities diary

◀ Keep a diary for 24 hours of the activities given below.

   ☐ Use the recording chart to help.

   ☐ Remember that you may do some things more than once a day.

◀ Calculate the time you spent doing these things in a day. How long do you think you would spend on them over a week or a month or a year?

◀ Choose your own activities to add to the table. You can use a calculator.

Activity	Time	Time spent	Total for 24 hours
Playing football	11:15 – 12:10	55 mins	
Sleeping			
Eating			
Washing/bathing			
Exercising			
Watching TV/ using computer			

BLOCK D

Dear Helper
This is an exercise in calculating times using the 24-hour clock. Remind your child that pm times are the second set of 12 hours in 24, so 1.30pm is written as 13:30. It is an interesting exercise to find out what proportion of our lives we spend sleeping or eating! Some children may need support with the calculating, remembering that there are 60 minutes to the next hour. Encourage them to 'count on' in units of five minutes up to the next hour and then count on in hours.

Name   Date

X marks the spot!

◾ This is a map Captain Jack had in his sea chest. The X near the top left corner of the island shows where the buried treasure lies.

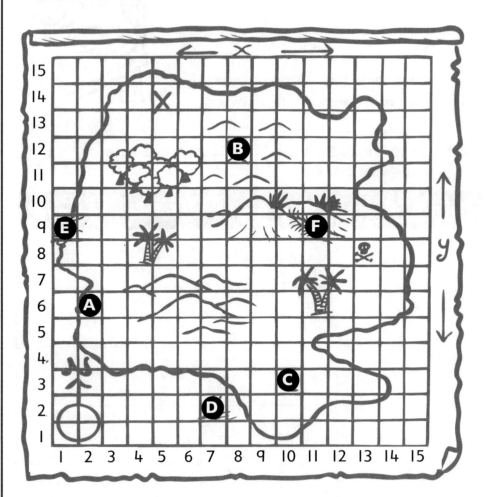

◾ What are the coordinates of the following places?

A Spy-glass Point ☐   **B** One Tree Hill ☐

C Gallows Point ☐   **D** Shark Bay ☐

E Ragged Rocks ☐   **F** Dead Man's Alley ☐

◾ Captain Jack digs up the buried treasure but needs to hide it from his ghastly crew! He buries it again at (11,12). Write an 'x' on the map to mark this spot.

Dear Helper
This activity helps your child to read and plot coordinates. Children often get confused over which axis to read first. Coordinates always read along the x axis first. A good way to remember this is to say 'across first', meaning the 'x' is a 'cross'. As an extension to this activity, ask your child to add some landmarks of their own to the island, giving them names and noting their coordinates.

Securing number facts, relationships and calculating

Activity name	Learning objectives	Managing the homework
E1		
Factor trees Sort numbers into their factor pairs and display them like the branches of a tree.	Identify pairs of factors of two-digit whole numbers and find common multiples (for example, for 6 and 9)	**Before:** Ensure the children understand the meaning of the word 'factor'. Some may require table squares to support their work. **After:** Check through the homework with the class. Make sure that the factors are given in pairs. Ask: *Which numbers have an oddd number of factors? Why?*
Shape fractions Match the shape pictures and fractions.	Express a smaller whole number as a fraction of a larger one (for example, recognise that 5 out of 8 is $5/8$); find equivalent fractions (for example, $7/10 = 14/20$, or $19/10 = 1 9/10$)	**Before:** Suggest to the children that they match the shapes and fractions with a pencil line first, before colouring the shapes, to ensure each fraction has a matching shape. **After:** Ask for different choices of matching shapes. Ask: *Which pictures had more than one fraction?*
Magic squares Investigate number patterns and attempt to explain and predict.	Represent a problem by identifying and recording the calculations needed to solve it; find possible solutions and confirm them in the context of the problem	**Before:** Explain the rules of magic squares. **After:** Share some examples. Discuss whether there is more than one solution to the squares.
Tables builder Build knowledge of 12-, 13- and 14-times tables from the 10- and 2-, 3- and 4-times tables.	Extend mental methods for whole-number calculations, for example to multiply a two-digit number by a one-digit number (for example, 12 × 9), to multiply by 25 (for example, 16 × 25)	**Before:** Ask the children to remind you of useful links between times tables that they have recently explored. **After:** Ask the children to suggest further developments using these links, such as finding multiples of 22, 24 or 26.
Fractions and decimals Link equivalent fractions and decimals (eg $1/10 = 0.1$ and $1/2 = 5/10 = 0.5$).	Relate fractions to their decimal representations	**Before:** Show the children how a calculator can assist when finding fraction/decimal equivalents. **After:** Ask the children how many fraction/decimal equivalents they can remember.
Fashion sale now on! Find the cost of items after a percentage price reduction.	Find fractions using division (for example, $1/100$ of 5kg), and percentages of numbers and quantities (for example, 10%, 5% and 15% of £80)	**Before:** Discuss fraction and percentage equivalents. **After:** Discuss methods used to find the correct answers. Did the children first find 10% and then use that to work out other percentages?
E2		
Find the triples Play a pelmanism game with fractions, percentages and decimals.	Express a smaller whole number as a fraction of a larger one (for example, recognise that 5 out of 8 is $5/8$); find equivalent fractions (for example, $7/10 = 14/20$, or $19/10 = 1 9/10$); relate fractions to their decimal representations	**Before:** Explain the rules of pelmanism or pairs. **After:** Invite some children to say a fraction or decimal for the rest of the class to suggest its equivalent(s).
Ratio patterns Colour geometric patterns in a ratio of 3:2 or 3:6.	Solve problems involving proportions of quantities (for example, decrease quantities in a recipe designed to feed six people)	**Before:** Revise what a ratio is and how this will help them to colour their designs. **After:** Ask the children to calculate the total number of pieces in each colour and express each colour as a proportion.
Three of a kind Work out fractions, decimals and percentage equivalents.	• Relate fractions to their decimal representations • Understand percentage as the number of parts in every 100 and express tenths and hundredths as percentages	**Before:** Invite the children to explain the equivalents they are comfortable with using from the class lesson. **After:** Ask the children if they have committed to memory any new equivalents.

Securing number facts, relationships and calculating

Activity name	Learning objectives	Managing the homework
Special offers Compare offers from three shops and decide which offers the best deal.	Understand percentage as the number of parts in every 100 and express tenths and hundredths as percentages	**Before:** Discuss how advertisements aim to encourage people to think that they are getting a good deal. **After:** Discuss the children's findings and investigate the extension activity.
A collection of parts Collect examples of percentages and fractions in ads, newspaper headlines and so on.	• Relate fractions to their decimal representations • Understand percentage as the number of parts in every 100 and express tenths and hundredths as percentages	**Before:** Invite the children to suggest places where they have observed references to fractions, decimals and percentages in real life. **After:** Compare findings and create a class display.
Ratio problems Draw ratio pictures to illustrate given information.	Use sequences to scale numbers up or down; solve problems involving proportions of quantities (for example, decrease quantities in a recipe designed to feed six people)	**Before:** Remind the children how they drew ratios in class. Invite a demonstration. **After:** Share and check results.
E3		
Multiplication and division word problems Apply calculation methods to real-life situations and word problems.	Solve one-step and two-step problems involving whole numbers and decimals and all four operations, choosing and using appropriate calculation strategies, including calculator use	**Before:** Ask the children to remind you of various strategies that they might use when solving word problems. **After:** Invite some of the children to demonstrate the method they chose to solve some of the word problems.
Quantities for a recipe Increase the quantities of a simple recipe for six cakes to make 12 or 18 cakes.	Use sequences to scale numbers up or down; solve problems involving proportions of quantities (for example, decrease quantities in a recipe designed to feed six people)	**Before:** Emphasise the safety aspect of baking at home. Stress that an adult must be consulted. **After:** Invite the children to suggest a ratio for decorating their cakes (such as cherries to buttons 1:4), then ask them to calculate the numbers needed for 6, 12 and 18 cakes.
Fair play Make decisions about calculations based on a visit to a fair.	Solve one-step and two-step problems involving whole numbers and decimals and all four operations, choosing and using appropriate calculation strategies, including calculator use	**Before:** Discuss with the children possible ways of solving this problem. **After:** Compare the 'best value' findings and encourage the children to discuss reasons for their decisions.
Proportion problems Answer questions about percentages, ratio and proportion.	Solve problems involving proportions of quantities (for example, decrease quantities in a recipe designed to feed six people)	**Before:** Invite the children to remind you of the link between percentages and proportion and how to find a fraction of a number. **After:** Share results and invite the children who created some of their own questions to challenge the rest of the class.
Currencies around the world Find out which countries use the euro and investigate other currencies of the world, and their exchange rates.	• Solve one-step and two-step problems involving whole numbers and decimals and all four operations, choosing and using appropriate calculation strategies, including calculator use • Represent a problem by identifying and recording the calculations needed to solve it; find possible solutions and confirm them in the context of the problem	**Before:** Discuss with the class the various sources of information that might prove useful. **After:** Share the children's findings.
Swotty Simon's challenge Multiply and divide three-digit, two-digit and decimal numbers.	Refine and use efficient written methods to multiply and divide HTU × U, TU × TU, U.t × U and HTU ÷ U	**Before:** Go through some examples of the written methods of multiplication and division with the class. **After:** Discuss the children's answers to the questions on the worksheet. Ask: *Who beat Swotty Simon and won the challenge?*

■SCHOLASTIC

Name	Date

Factor trees

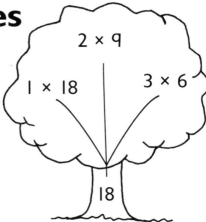

■ Factor trees are drawn by splitting up numbers into multiplication facts.

  ☐ Here is an example:

  "The factors of 18 are 1, 2, 3, 6, 9 and 18."

■ Use the drawings below to make factor trees for the following numbers: **24   28   36   40   64** and **85**.

Dear Helper

A factor is a number that will divide exactly into another number. Making these factor trees will help to improve your child's knowledge of times tables. The factors should be shown in pairs. Point out that all numbers have one and itself as factors, so 1 × the number is probably the best place to start. Avoid discussing 'prime numbers' and 'prime factors' at this stage. Work on these terms will follow later.

BLOCK E

Name   Date

Shape fractions

- Shade part of each shape and match the shape fraction to the appropriate number fraction.

- Draw a line to join each pair together.

Warning: some shape fractions may match more than one number fraction!

Shapes	Fractions

Column of shapes and column of fractions:

$$\frac{2}{5} \qquad \frac{3}{2} \qquad 1\frac{2}{3}$$

$$\frac{7}{5} \qquad \frac{5}{8} \qquad \frac{3}{3}$$

$$\frac{15}{10}$$

$$1\frac{3}{4} \qquad \frac{10}{6} \qquad 1\frac{1}{2}$$

$$\frac{3}{4} \qquad 1\frac{5}{8} \qquad \frac{1}{2}$$

$$\frac{13}{8}$$

Dear Helper

This activity helps your child to recall how fractions can appear visually, as parts of shapes, and to recognise equivalent fractions in the form of improper fractions (for example, $^{13}/_5$) and mixed numbers (such as $2^3/_5$). If your child is unable to remember how to convert from one to the other, remind them that the bottom number in a fraction is the number of pieces the shape has been cut into and the top number is the number of pieces they have got. So the improper fraction $^3/_2$, for example, is larger than 1. Fractions such as $^3/_3$, $^4/_4$ and $^5/_5$ are all equal to 1. As a challenge, suggest that your child tries to draw and name some shapes of their own.

Name	Date

Magic squares

■ This is a 'magic square':

4	3	8
9	5	1
2	7	6

- ☐ The total of the numbers in every row, column and diagonal is the same number: 15.

- ☐ 15 is the 'magic total' for this square.

■ Write down four things that you observe about this magic square. (For example, you might observe that the four corner numbers are even.)

1. _____

2. _____

3. _____

4. _____

■ Can you make up two more magic squares in the grids below, using the numbers 1 to 9? The 'magic total' can be 15 or any other number.

- ☐ Cut out the digit cards below to help you re-arrange the numbers.

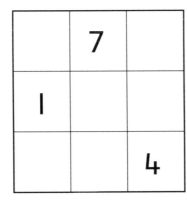

	7	
1		
		4

	1	
		7
		2

1	2	3	4	5	6	7	8	9

Dear Helper
Your child will have to solve this puzzle by using trial and error and remembering the rule of a magic square: that the numbers in all rows, columns and diagonals add up to the same total. Your child should be able to use knowledge of how numbers combine to help with this – for example, knowing that two odd numbers add to make an even number. Challenge your child to make up a magic square with a different total number.

Name	Date

Tables builder

■ Complete these times tables. You should know these already.

10×	**2×**	**3×**	**4×**
1 × 10 = 10	1 × 2 = 2	1 × 3 = 3	1 × 4 = 4
2 × 10 =	2 × 2 =	2 × 3 =	2 × 4 =
3 × 10 =	3 × 2 =	3 × 3 =	3 × 4 =
4 × 10 =	4 × 2 =	4 × 3 =	4 × 4 =
5 × 10 =	5 × 2 =	5 × 3 =	5 × 4 =
6 × 10 =	6 × 2 =	6 × 3 =	6 × 4 =
7 × 10 =	7 × 2 =	7 × 3 =	7 × 4 =
8 × 10 =	8 × 2 =	8 × 3 =	8 × 4 =
9 × 10 =	9 × 2 =	9 × 3 =	9 × 4 =
10 × 10 =	10 × 2 =	10 × 3 =	10 × 4 =

■ Now use those times tables to build up the following less well-known times tables.

12× = 10× + 2×	**13×** = 10× + 3×	**14×** = 10× + 4×	**15×** = 10× + 5×
1 × 12 =	1 × 13 =	1 × 14 =	1 × 15 =
2 × 12 =	2 × 13 =	2 × 14 =	2 × 15 =
3 × 12 =	3 × 13 =	3 × 14 =	3 × 15 =
4 × 12 =	4 × 13 =	4 × 14 =	4 × 15 =
5 × 12 =	5 × 13 =	5 × 14 =	5 × 15 =
6 × 12 =	6 × 13 =	6 × 14 =	6 × 15 =
7 × 12 =	7 × 13 =	7 × 14 =	7 × 15 =
8 × 12 =	8 × 13 =	8 × 14 =	8 × 15 =
9 × 12 =	9 × 13 =	9 × 14 =	9 × 15 =
10 × 12 =	10 × 13 =	10 × 14 =	10 × 15 =

Dear Helper

This is an exercise in building up times-tables knowledge from multiplication facts that your child already knows. If your child knows 2 × 10 and 2 × 4, then they can find 2 × 14 by adding these two results together. Encourage your child to work in a methodical way. If you feel a further challenge would be helpful, ask them to build the 21- or 22-times table.

BLOCK E

Name	Date

Fractions and decimals

◼ Link each fraction to its equivalent decimal with a coloured pencil line.

◼ Use your knowledge of decimals to do this. Use a calculator for any that you are not sure about.

$\frac{1}{10}$	0.5
$\frac{4}{10}$	0.2
$\frac{1}{5}$	0.9
$\frac{2}{10}$	0.75
$\frac{90}{100}$	0.33
$\frac{1}{2}$	0.2
$\frac{1}{4}$	0.5
$\frac{3}{4}$	0.7
$\frac{5}{10}$	0.3
$\frac{1}{3}$	0.4
$\frac{30}{100}$	0.1
$\frac{70}{100}$	0.25

BLOCK E

Dear Helper

This activity helps your child to remember what decimals are equivalent to some familiar fractions. It is very useful for your child to remember as many of these equivalents as possible, both for working out weights, measures and fractions of numbers and for work on percentages later this year. Challenge your child to see how many of the fraction–decimal pairs shown above they can recall without using the calculator.

Name   Date

Fashion sale now on!

◀ These items are offered in sales in two different shops.

◀ Kate wants to pay the lowest prices.

◀ Help her calculate which is the cheaper of the corresponding items in each shop. How much will she pay for each item that she decides to buy?

Dear Helper

This activity helps your child to find fractions and percentages of numbers and quantities – in this case, prices. You can practise this skill when out shopping with your child. Encourage them to look at discounts and sale prices. If a pair of trainers is labelled '40% off', ask them: *What was the original price?*

Name	Date

Find the triples

This is a game for two to four players.

■ Cut out the cards carefully and shuffle the pack.

  ☐ Place all the cards face down, spread evenly across the table.

  ☐ Take turns to turn over three cards.

  ☐ If all three cards are equivalent in value (for example, $\frac{1}{2}$ = 0.5 = 50%), keep them. If not, turn them back.

  ☐ The aim is to collect as many families of three as you can.

✂

$\frac{1}{10}$	0.1	10%	$\frac{2}{10}$	0.2
20%	$\frac{1}{4}$	0.25	25%	$\frac{1}{2}$
0.5	50%	$\frac{3}{10}$	0.3	
30%	$\frac{3}{4}$	0.75	75%	

Dear Helper

Please play this game with your child. Before you play, it might be helpful to make sure that you are both familiar with the equivalent values (for example, $^2/_{10}$ = 20% = 0.2 and ¼ = 0.25 = 25%). This activity will help your child to recognise equivalent fractions, decimals and percentages and be able to swap from one to another when calculating. If your child has difficulty recognising all three equivalents, remove the percentage cards to begin with and remind them to convert all the fractions to tenths to work out the decimal. A further challenge might be to extend the pack by finding other decimal equivalents, using a calculator, and converting them to percentages.

BLOCK E

Name   Date

Ratio patterns

◼ Colour these two patterns. For each pattern, use two colours in the given ratio.

A ratio of 3:2

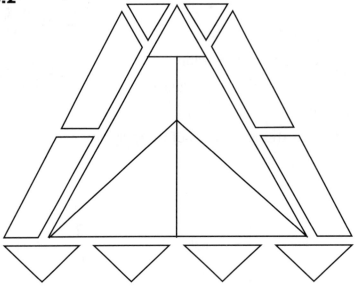

A ratio of 3:6

Dear Helper
If your child is unsure how to colour in the patterns, please remind them that a ratio is '...for every...'.
So, for example, a ratio of 2:3 would be two red pieces for every three green pieces. To challenge your
child further, encourage them to look for ratio patterns in everyday life – for example, pieces of cutlery to
plates at the table, or sausages to eggs on a plate.

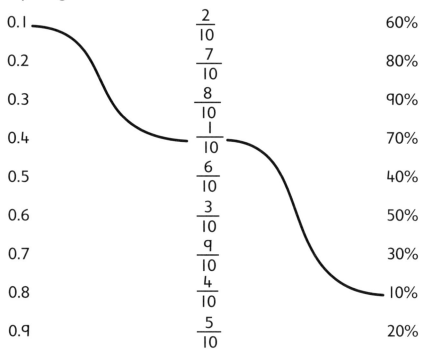

Name	Date

Three of a kind

◼ Draw lines to link the equivalent decimals, fractions and percentages. One trio has been joined up for you.

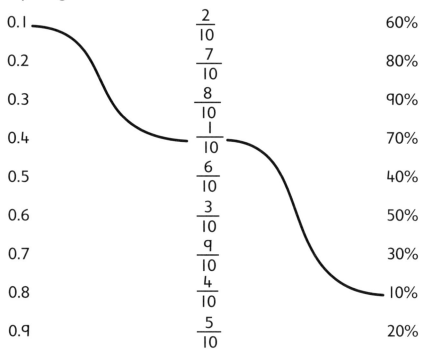

0.1	$\frac{2}{10}$	60%
0.2	$\frac{7}{10}$	80%
0.3	$\frac{8}{10}$	90%
0.4	$\frac{1}{10}$	70%
0.5	$\frac{6}{10}$	40%
0.6	$\frac{3}{10}$	50%
0.7	$\frac{9}{10}$	30%
0.8	$\frac{4}{10}$	10%
0.9	$\frac{5}{10}$	20%

◼ Draw lines to link the matching amounts. One trio has been joined up for you.

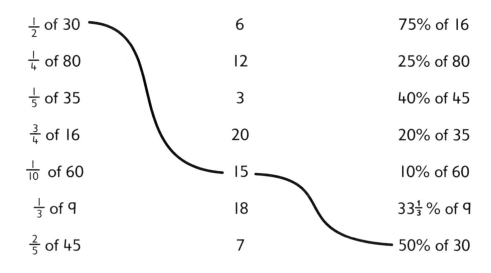

$\frac{1}{2}$ of 30	6	75% of 16
$\frac{1}{4}$ of 80	12	25% of 80
$\frac{1}{5}$ of 35	3	40% of 45
$\frac{3}{4}$ of 16	20	20% of 35
$\frac{1}{10}$ of 60	15	10% of 60
$\frac{1}{3}$ of 9	18	$33\frac{1}{3}$ % of 9
$\frac{2}{5}$ of 45	7	50% of 30

BLOCK E

Dear Helper

This activity will help your child to see the links between fractions, decimals and percentages, and show them that they can work out a percentage of an amount by converting it into a fraction (for example, 50% of £10 is $\frac{1}{2}$ of £10 = £5). If your child is struggling, it might be helpful to remind them that the fraction $\frac{1}{10}$ is the same as the decimal 0.1, which is the same as 10%. If your child finds the activity easy, challenge them to think of some other fractions to find the percentage equivalents of – for example, $\frac{1}{4}$ or $\frac{2}{3}$.

Name	Date

Special offers

Sam's Sale 20% off everything!

CHEAP & CHEERFUL 25% OFF THE MOST EXPENSIVE ITEM.

BARGAIN BASEMENT PRICES CUT BY $\frac{1}{4}$.

◼ Look at the advertisements above.

◼ Which shop is offering the best reductions? _____

◼ Explain in words how you know: _____

_____

◼ Calculate the cost of buying a pair of gloves and a scarf from each shop.
  ☐ The pre-sale prices were £8.50 for the gloves and £7.25 for the scarf.

Shop	Gloves	Scarf
Sam's Sale		
Bargain Basement		
Cheap & Cheerful		

Dear Helper
This real-life problem helps your child to reason about numbers and make decisions. You can help your child by reminding them of the relevant fraction/percentage equivalents, such as $^1/_4$ = 25%. A further challenge might be to increase the number of items bought from each shop and ask your child how expensive the most expensive item has to be in order for Cheap & Cheerful to give better value than Bargain Basement.

Name	Date

A collection of parts

◼ Make a collection of pictures, advertisements, leaflets, newspaper headlines and so on, that mention percentages and fractions.

◼ Display them as a collage, either on the sheet below or on a larger sheet if you prefer.

BLOCK E

Dear Helper

Fractions and percentages are often displayed in shops and in advertisements, but many people find them difficult to understand and use. This activity is designed to make fractions and percentages more 'real' to your child. Newspapers and magazines are the best places to start looking. You might like to challenge your child to calculate some of the price reductions being advertised. Or if your child finds the whole concept of fractions and percentages difficult, discuss with them what the advertised price reductions mean.

Name   Date

Ratio problems

■ Draw ratio pictures to show the following:

1. There are 12 cats in a ratio of 1:5 ginger to black.

2. There are 21 children in a ratio of 1:2 boys to girls.

3. There are 16 sailing boats in a ratio 3:5 white sails to red sails.

4. There are 15 flowers in a ratio 1:4 blue to yellow.

PHOTOCOPIABLE ■SCHOLASTIC

Name	Date

Multiplication and division word problems

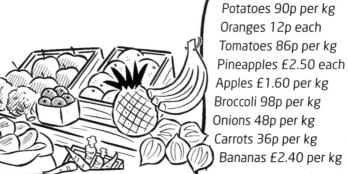

Potatoes 90p per kg
Oranges 12p each
Tomatoes 86p per kg
Pineapples £2.50 each
Apples £1.60 per kg
Broccoli 98p per kg
Onions 48p per kg
Carrots 36p per kg
Bananas £2.40 per kg

◼ Answer these questions. Show how you worked them out.

◼ You can use different methods to answer different questions.

1. How much do these things cost?

5kg of potatoes	Six oranges	Four pineapples	500g of bananas

2. How much do these things cost?

One banana if five bananas weigh 1kg	One apple if four apples weigh 1kg	4kg of carrots	3kg of tomatoes

3. I am going to make some soup for my friends. This is the recipe. How much will it cost me to buy all the vegetables?

500g carrots
2kg potatoes
500g onions
3kg tomatoes

BLOCK E

Dear Helper

This activity will help your child to use different methods for multiplication and division. Please encourage your child to use the methods learned at school, such as the grid method for multiplying, or division by 'chunking' (ie dividing part of the number using a known times table, and then subtracting it from the original number). If your child is unable to remember a method, please do not try to teach them the way you were taught as this will only lead to confusion. If your child finds these calculations difficult, encourage them to multiply by repeated addition, or by counting in steps (of 2, 3 and so on). A more able child could be encouraged to make up further, more complicated shopping list calculations.

Name   Date

Quantities for a recipe

◼ Here is a recipe to make six small sponge cakes.

◼ How would you increase the quantities of the ingredients
to make 12 or 18 cakes?

☐ Remember to keep the quantities of the different ingredients in the same ratio.

To make 6 small sponge cakes, you will need:	To make 12 small sponge cakes, you will need:	To make 18 small sponge cakes, you will need:
50g self-raising flour	_____ g self-raising flour	_____ g self-raising flour
50g soft margarine	_____ g soft margarine	_____ g soft margarine
50g caster sugar	_____ g caster sugar	_____ g caster sugar
1 egg	_____ eggs	_____ eggs
1 tablespoon cocoa	_____ tablespoons cocoa	_____ tablespoons cocoa
6 paper cake cases	_____ paper cake cases	_____ paper cake cases

SAFETY WARNING: Ask an adult to help you with the hot oven.

Wash your hands before you start. However many cakes you make, the
method is the same.

1. Beat the margarine and sugar together in a large mixing bowl until the mixture
is smooth and creamy. You can do this with a wooden spoon or an electric whisk.

2. Beat in the egg, a little at a time. If the mixture becomes wet and slimy, beat in
a spoonful of the flour.

3. When all the egg has been mixed in, sieve the flour and cocoa into the mixture
and stir in gently with a large metal spoon.

4. Place the cake cases in a cake tin and divide the mixture between the cases.

5. Bake in a hot oven at 180°C (or gas mark 5) for 12 to 15 minutes.

6. Your cakes are cooked when they are bouncy and springy to the touch. Leave
them to cool on a wire rack. The cakes can be eaten as they are, or with a little
icing on the top.

BLOCK E

Dear Helper
This activity demonstrates one way that ratios are used in daily life. The recipe will not work if the
amount of one ingredient is increased without increasing the other ingredients in the same proportion.
If you and your child make the cakes, show them how to work safely and hygienically in the kitchen, then
share the cakes! Children who find this easy might enjoy converting other recipes (for example, altering
quantities for a curry for four people to make it for six or two or three people).

Name   Date

Fair play

- Look at the special offers below.
- Which offer gives the best value for money (the lowest cost per ride)?

Freddo's Fun Fair

All rides £1.50 each

or

three rides for £4.45

or

five rides for £7.75

or

six rides for £8.40

or

ten rides for £14.90

- Best value: _____

  Because _____

  _____

- Poorest value: _____

  Because _____

  _____

BLOCK E

Dear Helper

This is a real-life problem for your child to solve by calculating. Your child needs to calculate the unit price (the price of each ride) for each offer. Alternatively, they could simply multiply the number of rides by £1.50 each time and compare that with the special offer. So they can choose whether to use division or multiplication – as long as they do so correctly! For children who find this difficult, you may need to convert each problem into a number calculation for them – for example, to find the unit price £4.45 ÷ 3. As a further challenge, talk about the discount offers in supermarkets. Do they always save you money? Why not?

Name	Date

Proportion problems

◼ Solve these proportion problems. Show your working out.

1. Of 100 people, 5% were unhappy about the amount of litter in their town.

What proportion, and how many people, were quite happy?

```
                                                    _____

                                                    _____
```

2. Of 110 chairs in a school hall, 10% have wobbly legs.

What proportion are safe and sound? How many chairs is that?

```
                                                    _____

                                                    _____
```

3. Eighty per cent of a group of 40 women said they owned a hat.

How many owned a hat? What proportion did not?

```
                                                    _____

                                                    _____
```

4. Ninety-five per cent of a group of 500 children own a pet.

What proportion do not own a pet? How many children are not pet owners?

```
                                                    _____

                                                    _____
```

Dear Helper

This activity helps your child to understand the idea of proportion. A proportion represents a certain number 'out of' a total. Percentages take this a step further, expressing a proportion as a number out of 100 (whatever the actual total number is). For example, the proportion 4 out of 5 is equal to 80%. Encourage your child to express these proportions in their simplest form. For example, $80\% = {}^{80}/_{100} = {}^{8}/_{10} = {}^{4}/_{5}$. If your child is finding these difficult, remind them that percentages can be broken down into 'lots of 10%'. For example, to find 10% of a number we divide that number by 10, so 10% of 50 is 5. We can use this knowledge to find 20% (double it =10) or 5% (halve it = 2.5). Challenge your child to make up some more proportion questions to share at school.

Name	Date

Currencies around the world

■ Find out more about different currencies around the world.

■ List the countries and currencies you find in the table below.

Country	Currency	Exchange rate

■ How many countries in Europe use the euro? List them in the box below.

■ If you received £5.00 pocket money,
how much would this be in:

US dollars	
Yen	
euros	
other	

Dear Helper
You will find information about currencies and exchange rates in newspapers, atlases, teletext and on the internet. You may help your child by using a calculator for the conversions. Some children may find the conversions difficult. It may help to remind them about ratio: *For every pound I get _____.* This will then need to be multiplied by 5 to find the equivalent of £5. A further challenge might be to discover some more obscure currencies to convert.

Name	Date

Swotty Simon's challenge

■ Swotty Simon has scored 7 out of 8 in this maths test. He doesn't think anyone can beat his score. Go on, prove him wrong!

1)   **683**
     x 7

2)   **829**
     x 9

3)   **45**
     x 63

4)   **84**
     x 29

5)   **2.7**
     x 5

6)   **7.3**
     x 3

7) 3⟌693

8) 7⟌224

Dear Helper

This activity helps your child to consolidate the 'efficient written methods' of long multiplication and division – the methods you and your parents were probably taught at school! If they are still having trouble then go through the method carefully step by step and provide as much practice as your child needs. It is really important that these skills are established before going into Year 6 and beyond.

Puzzles and problems: Objectives grid

The puzzles and problems activities can be used very flexibly to provide children with fun maths tasks to take home. The puzzles and problems are based on work that children will be covering during the year and should test their use and application of mathematics at an appropriate level. Where possible, children should be encouraged to try different approaches to solving these problems and to look for clues and patterns in mathematics.

The grid below lists each activity and identifies links to the different objectives within the Using and applying mathematics strand of the Renewed Framework.

	Solve one-step and two-step problems involving whole numbers and decimals and all four operations, choosing and using appropriate calculation strategies, including calculator use	Represent a puzzle or problem by identifying and recording the data or calculations needed to solve it; find possible solutions and confirm them in the context of the problem	Plan and pursue an enquiry; present evidence by collecting, organising and interpreting information; suggest extensions to the enquiry	Explore patterns, properties and relationships and propose a general statement involving numbers or shapes; identify examples for which the statement is true or false	Explain reasoning using diagrams, graphs and text; refine ways of recording using images and symbols
1 Robin Hood	✔				
2 She sells sea shells	✔				
3 Piggy banks	✔				
4 Ice dance	✔				
5 Sports day	✔				
6 Walking the dog	✔				
7 Wipe-out!	✔				
8 Pharoah puzzle				✔	
9 Factor finder				✔	
10 Page turner	✔				
11 5p and 10p	✔				
12 Kitchen floor				✔	
13 Dealing with decimals	✔				
14 Tile trial				✔	
15 Computer games sale!	✔				
16 In the kitchen			✔		
17 Match the target			✔		
18 Kilos to grams	✔			✔	
19 How likely?			✔		
20 Loaded dice				✔	
21 All the way round			✔		
22 Happy birthday!		✔			
23 Up, up and away!		✔		✔	
24 Kittens	✔				
25 Measure me			✔		
26 Apple pie	✔				
27 Long jump	✔				
28 Pushbike puzzle	✔				
29 Find the numbers		✔		✔	
30 Rings of 15				✔	
31 Nature watch	✔		✔		
32 Maths test	✔				
33 Javelin throw	✔				
34 Pancakes		✔			
35 School dinners	✔				
36 Skateboard scurry	✔				

1 Robin Hood

Which two targets does Robin need to hit in order to score exactly 1000 points and win the Golden Arrow?

2 She sells sea shells

Sashi sells sea shells by the sea shore for 58p per bag.

Shelley buys three bags of shells and pays with a £5 note.

How much change does she get?

Puzzles and problems

3 Piggy banks

Twin brothers Barry and Gary empty their piggy banks.

There is £7.47 in one and £9.59 in the other.

How much do the brothers have in total?

4 Ice dance

Tanya receives the following scores for her ice-dance routine:

0.4, 1.9, 1.2, 0.7, and 1.5.

Which score is the closest to 1?

5 Sports day

Here are the recorded times for the 100m final at St Swifts' School sports day.

Mike: 15.23 secs
Jack: 15.13 secs
Anthony: 16.33 secs
Ciaran: 16.21 secs
Peter: 15.32 secs
Leroy: 15.73 secs

Who won and who came last?

_____

_____

6 Walking the dog

Terry got 30p from his dad every time he took their dog for a walk.

Terry had saved £6.

How many times had he walked the dog?

_____

Puzzles and problems

7 Wipe-out!

Someone has wiped out some digits from this calculation on the board.

Help the teacher fill them in correctly.

8 Pharaoh puzzle

Pharaoh Ahbygum the Third was shown some possible nets of his soon-to-be-built pyramid.

Only one net will actually make a square-based pyramid.

Which one should he choose?

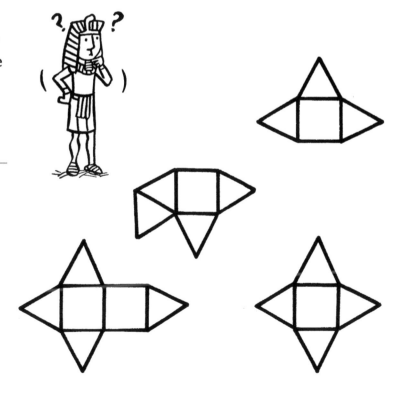

9 Factor finder

Femi says that he has found all of the factors of the age of his dad who is 32.

He found four factors.

Femi's dad says he's wrong and that there are five factors.

Can you find the correct answer?

_____

_____

_____

_____

_____

10 Page turner

Lily has read 138 pages of her book, _Planting Vegetables_ by Rosa Beans.

The book is 320 pages long.

How many more pages has Lily got to read before she finishes the book?

_____

Puzzles and problems

11 5p and 10p

Karen has collected £1.85 in 5p and 10p coins.

She has nine 5p coins. How many 10p coins does she have?

12 Kitchen floor

Tyler needs to lay three more tiles on this kitchen floor.

However, they must be symmetrical in both mirror lines.

Shade in squares on this plan so that Tyler can lay his tiles correctly.

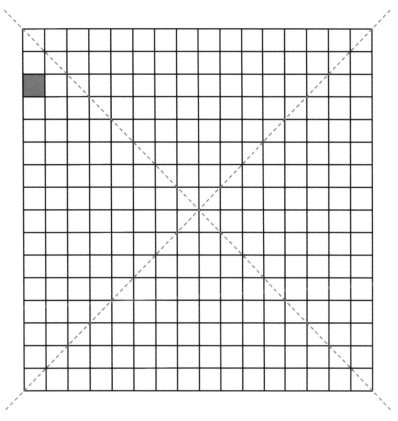

13 Dealing with decimals

Magical Misty is thinking of a number.

He halves it, adds 0.7 and comes up with the answer 6.4.

What number did Magical Misty start with?

14 Tile trial

Tyler has just started a new flooring job.

How many tiles does he need to surround the three he has already laid?

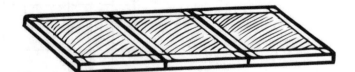

15 Computer games sale!

X-station games are on special offer: *Call to Duty* is £12.69, *Chronic the Hedgehog* is £14.37 and *Virtual Knitting 2* is £16.75.

Mehmet has £50 to spend for his birthday and buys all three.

How much change does he get?

16 In the kitchen

You will need a set of kitchen scales for this one.

Find an everyday food item like an apple.

Estimate its weight, and then weigh it. How close were you?

Now estimate the weight of three apples and weigh them. Were you close?

17 Match the target

You will need a set of kitchen scales.

Your challenge is to find an object that weighs exactly 275g.

Look at each object before you weigh it and try to estimate how much it will weigh.

How many tries did it take you to find a 275g object?

Now try to find something that weighs exactly 500g.

18 Kilos to grams

Liam has weighed himself and he has found that he weighs 32.6kg.

Danny asks him how much this is in grams, as he weighs 35,700g.

Who is heavier and by how many grams?

Puzzles and problems

19 How likely?

Vicky says that she is certain the sun will rise tomorrow.

Laura says that she is certain her lucky numbers will win the lottery.

Chantelle says she is certain her dad will bring home her favourite comic.

Only one of them is using 'certain' correctly. Which one?

_____

20 Loaded dice

Dicey Dave has made a six-sided dice that is very unlikely to roll an even number.

Write six numbers that he could put on the dice to make this statement true.

_____

_____

_____

_____

_____

_____

21 All the way round

Estimate the perimeter, or distance around, your bedroom in centimetres.

Now measure the perimeter with a ruler or tape measure. Be as accurate as you can.

How close was your estimate?

Give yourself a pat on the back if you were within 50cm!

22 Happy birthday!

Kim's birthday was on Tuesday, 5 January.

To celebrate she went to the cinema with her friends the following Sunday.

What was the date of their cinema trip?

Puzzles and problems

23 Up, up and away!

Steve takes off in his hot air balloon at 07.45.

He lands safely at 14.26.

How long was his flight in hours and minutes?

24 Kittens

Three little kittens each weigh 885g, 0.76kg and 636g.

How much do they weigh altogether?

25 Measure me

I am an irregular pentagon.

Measure each of my sides with a ruler and find the distance around me to the nearest millimetre.

_____

26 Apple pie

Sally picked 3.6kg of apples.

She then made four apple pies, each containing the same amount of apple.

How many grams of apple does each pie contain?

_____

Puzzles and problems

27 Long jump

Chaya jumped 2.26m in the long jump on sports day.

Her friend Grace jumped 83cm further.

How far did Grace jump in metres?

28 Pushbike puzzle

Tom has completed $\frac{7}{10}$ of a 50km road race.

How far has Tom got to cycle before he gets to the finish line?

29 Find the numbers

Ian has found a pair of numbers with a sum of 15 and a product of 54.

Which two numbers are they?

_____

30 Rings of 15

Place each of the numbers 1 to 9 in the rings so that each ring has a total of 15.

(Only use each number once.)

_____

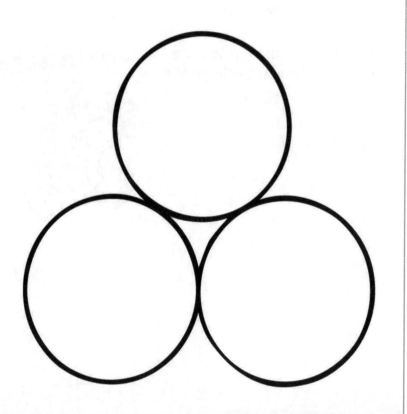

Puzzles and problems

31 Nature watch

Ben studied the wildlife in his garden.

Over the course of the afternoon he saw 4 cats, 11 birds, 1 fox and 6 spiders.

How many legs did the animals Ben saw have in total?

32 Maths test

Bruce scored 65% in his maths test.

In the same test, Patti answered $\frac{3}{4}$ of her questions correctly.

Stevie got half of his answers correct.

Who got the best test result?

33 Javelin throw

Tessa threw her javelin 46.56m.

Paula threw her javelin exactly half the distance that Tessa did.

How far was Paula's throw?

34 Pancakes

This recipe makes twelve pancakes:

100g flour

2 eggs

200ml water

50g butter

Change the recipe so that you can make 36 pancakes.

35 School dinners

At Hungry Street Primary School 10% of the children bring a packed lunch.

The rest have school dinners.

There are 120 pupils at the school.

How many children have school dinners?

36 Skateboard scurry

In 2008, 18-year-old Ben Stiff became both the fastest and youngest to travel the 980 miles from Land's End to John O'Groats on a skateboard.

When he had travelled 40 miles a day for 18 days, how much further did he have to go?

Block A

P9 **Investigating place value** Two digits: 28, 82; 67, 76;

Three digits: 459, 495, 549, 594, 945, 954; 168, 186, 618, 681, 816, 861;

Four digits: 3578, 3587, 3758, 3785, 3857, 3875, 5378, 5387, 5738, 5783, 5837, 5873, 7358, 7385, 7538, 7583, 7835, 7853, 8357, 8375, 8537, 8573, 8735, 8753; 0347, 0374, 0437, 0473, 0734, 0743, 3047, 3074, 3407, 3470, 3704, 3740, 4037, 4073, 4307, 4370, 4703, 4730, 7034, 7043, 7304, 7340, 7403, 7430.

P10 **Aim high** No answers.

P11 **The differences game** Answers will vary.

P12 **Take it away!** **1** 242; **2** 413; **3** 1114; **4** 2147; **5** 469; **6** 828; **7(a)** 1006; **(b)** 152.

P13 **Number chains** **1** 1, 1, 1; **2** 2, 1, 3, 3; **3** 2, 1, 1, 2; **4** 43, 48, 53; **5** 82, 72, 62; **6** −9, −12, −15; **7** 29, 37, 46.

P14 **Where is the hottest place?** Temperatures in ascending order: −2 < −1 < 0 < 4 < 5 < 6 = 6 < 8 < 10 = 10 < 11 = 11 < 13 = 13 < 15 < 18 < 20 = 20 < 21 < 22 < 23 < 24 < 25 < 34.

P15 **Number search**

16	18	19	21	385
894	141	6	204	401
59	60	61	64	399
112	138	912	249	403
897	913	933	935	226
1001	81	78	77	76
999	206	189	177	179
989	167	888	42	214
1004	188	186	194	187
566	581	612	601	26

P16 **Colour, add and win** Answers will vary.

P17 **Use what you know** Answers will vary.

P18 **Painting by multiples** Multiples of 6 (red): 12, 36; multiples of 7 (blue): 7, 14, 21, 28, 35, 49; multiples of 8 (yellow): 8, 16, 32, 64; multiples of 9 (purple): 9, 18, 27, 45; multiples of 10 (orange): 10, 20, 30, 40.

P19 **What's left?** **1** 66 r3 = 66¾ = 66.75ml; **2(a)** 83 r2 = 83²/₅ = 83.4; **(b)** 107 r9 = 107⁹/₁₀ = 107.9; **(c)** 70 r1 = 70½ = 70.5; **(d)** 36 r1 = 36¼ = 36.25; **3** 156¼ = 156.25cm; **4** £33.40.

P20 **Restaurant rip off!** **1** £241; **2** £60.25.

Block B

P23 **Times-table challenge**

×	2	3	4	5	6	7	8
2	4	6	8	10	12	14	16
4	8	12	16	20	24	28	32
8	16	24	32	40	48	56	64
3	6	9	12	15	18	21	24
6	12	18	24	30	36	42	48
9	18	27	36	45	54	63	72

×	3	4	5	6	7	8	9
4	12	16	20	24	28	32	36
5	15	20	25	30	35	40	45
9	27	36	45	54	63	72	81
3	9	12	15	18	21	24	27
7	21	28	35	42	49	56	63
2	6	8	10	12	14	16	18

×	4	5	6	7	8	9	10
2	8	10	12	14	16	18	20
3	12	15	18	21	24	27	30
4	16	20	24	28	32	36	40
5	20	25	30	35	40	45	50
6	24	30	36	42	48	54	60
7	28	35	42	49	56	63	70

×	6	5	7	8	9	3	4
8	48	40	56	64	72	24	32
4	24	20	28	32	36	12	16
5	30	25	35	40	45	15	20
9	54	45	63	72	81	27	36
7	42	35	49	56	63	21	28
6	36	30	42	48	54	18	24

P24 **Sorting triangles** Equilateral triangles have three equal sides, three equal angles; isosceles triangles have two sides of equal length, one side different length; scalene triangles have no equal sides; yes.

P25 **Sort them out**

	even number	factor of 24	<8	odd number
square number	16	4	1	9
>6	14	8	7	13
multiple of 3	6	12	3	15
<12	10	2	5	11

P26 **Calculations page** 559; 767; 1033; 185; 373; 1166; 4910.

P27 **Card trick** Numbers left over: 1, 5, 7, 11, 13.

P28 **You're the teacher** He scored 1 out of 7 (only question 3 was correct). Correct answers for other questions are: **1** £5.66; **2** £7.95; **4** £15.47; **5** £11.24; **6** £105.59; **7** £144.33.

Homework answers

P29 **Carl's chocolate chips** 46

P30 **Multiple sort** No answers.

P31 **Reflect on that**

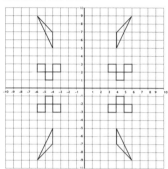

P32 **Flip it!**

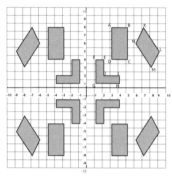

P33 **Thinking of a number** **1** 15; **2** 12; **3** 7.4; **4** 27.5; **5** 76; **6** 100.

P34 **Shape nets**

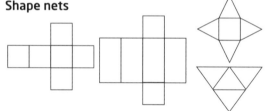

P35 **Number creatures** Answers will vary.

P36 **The school barbecue** **1** £168.25; **2** £156.79; **3** £325.04; **4** £405.64; **5** £1094.36.

P37 **Target number game** Answers will vary.

P38 **Colour me odd or even?**

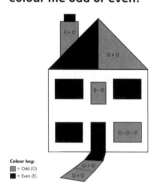

P39 **Viewing times** 178,000; 374,000; 473,000; 835,000; 473,000; 628,000; 935,000; 462,000; 815,000; 992,000.
1 651,000; **2** 1,465,000; **3** 1,770,000; **4** 1,443,000; **5** 836,000.

P40 **Drawing shapes** **1** rhombus, kite or irregular quadrilateral; **2** right-angled triangle (could be

isosceles); **3** irregular pentagon; **4** irregular hexagon; **5** irregular septagon; **6** regular hexagon.

Block C

P43 **Collecting and representing data** Answers will vary.

P44 **Weights and measures** Answers will vary.

P45 **Ordering masses** Answers will vary.

P46 **How much?** **1** 9kg; **2** 10m; **3** 21.42km; 42.84km; 214.2km; **4** 69 litres; 32 litres.

P47 **Every graph tells a story** Answers will vary.

P48 **That's impossible!** **1** unlikely; **2** certain; **3** impossible; **4** likely; **5** unlikely (although answers will vary!); **6** impossible; **7** certain; **8** unlikely; **9** impossible.

P49 **How long?** Answers will vary.

P50 **Problems with peas, pins, paper and pennies!** Answers will vary.

P51 **Comparing data** **1** 15°C; **2** 10°C; **3** London 13°C, Athens 28°C; **4/5** A line graph is used to show how something measurable, such as temperature, changes over a period of time, whereas a bar chart or a bar line graph is used to compare numbers of separate things, such as cars or different colour eyes.

P52 **Missing data** **3** 247; **5** 16°C.

P53 **Fruit facts** **1** 7; **2** bananas 18, pears 17, apples 4, satsumas 29, grapes 32; **3** grapes; **4** apples.

P54 **Sort it!** **1** 121; **2** 85; **3** 2; **4** 206.

Block D

P57 **24 hours** Answers will vary.

P58 **Telling the time** Answers will vary.

P59 **Finding areas** 6cm × 4cm = 24cm²; 5m × 8m = 40m²; 10cm × 0.8m = 0.08m² or 800cm²; 2m × 0.007km = 14m²; composite shapes: (5cm × 1cm = 5cm²) + (3cm × 3cm = 9cm²) = 14cm²; (5cm × 1cm = 5cm²) + (4cm × 1cm = 4cm²) = 9cm².

P60 **Living space** Answers will vary.

P61 **Looking at lines** Answers will vary.

P62 **Missing angles** **1** 80°; **2** 30°; **3** 50°; **4** 90°; **5** 50°; **6** 50°; **7** 35°; **8** 30°; **9** 90°; **10** 38°.

P63 **All at sea!** **1** 1050; **2** 2048; **3** 2550; **4** 4608; **5** 1092; **6** 3365; **7** 2688.

P64 **Acute, obtuse or right?** **1** right angle; **2** acute; **3** obtuse; **4** obtuse; **5** acute; **6** obtuse; **7** acute; **8** acute; **9** obtuse.

P65 **More times** 146 × 13 = 1898; 281 × 15 = 4215; 207 × 26 = 5382;

318 × 14 = 4452; 342 × 15 = 5130;
318 × 23 = 7314; 39.21 × 15 = 588.15;
142.63 × 12 = 1711.56; 35.39 × 21 = 743.19;
127.27 × 16 = 2036.32.

P66   Translate and reflect

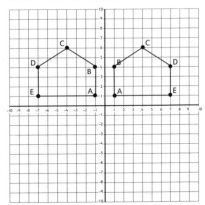

P67   Activities diary Answers will vary.

P68   X marks the spot! A (2,6); **B** (8,12); **C** (10,3); **D** (7,2); **E** (1,9); **F** (11,9). Check that correct new location of buried treasure has been marked at (11,12) on the grid.

Block E

P71   Factor trees 24 = 1 × 24; 2 × 12; 3 × 8; 4 × 6
28 = 1 × 28; 2 × 14; 4 × 7
36 = 1 × 36; 2 × 18; 3 × 12; 4 × 9; 6 × 6
40 = 1 × 40; 2 × 20; 4 × 10; 5 × 8
64 = 1 × 64; 2 × 32; 4 × 16; 8 × 8
85 = 1 × 85; 5 × 17.

P72   Shape fractions Answers may vary, but ensure coloured shapes match linked fractions.

P73   Magic squares Four facts: centre edge and opposite numbers = 10; diagonal corners add to make 10; corner numbers are even; centre number of each set of three numbers is odd.

P74   Tables builder Less well-known times tables:
12×: 12, 24, 36, 48, 60, 72, 84, 96, 108, 120;
13×: 13, 26, 39, 52, 65, 78, 91, 104, 117, 130;
14×: 14, 28, 42, 56, 70, 84, 98, 112, 126, 140;
15×: 15, 30, 45, 60, 75, 90, 105, 120, 135, 150.

P75   Fractions and decimals

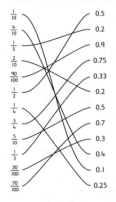

P76   Fashion sale now on! Dress £60; shoes £15; handbag £20; necklace £70; perfume £12.

P77   Find the triples No answers.

P78   Ratio patterns Answers will vary.

P79   Three of a kind

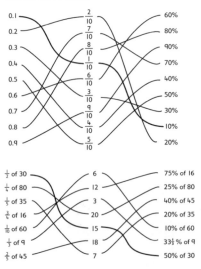

P80   Special offers Best reductions offered by Bargain Basement (£6.38 for gloves and £5.44 for the scarf); Sam's Sale: £6.80 (gloves) and £5.80 (scarf); Cheap & Cheerful: £6.38 (gloves) and £7.25 (scarf).

P81   A collection of parts Answers will vary.

P82   Ratio problems Pictures should show: **1** 2 ginger cats, 10 black ones; **2** 7 boys, 14 girls; **3** 6 sailing boats with white sails, 10 with red sails; **4** 3 blue flowers, 12 yellow ones.

P83   Multiplication and division word problems
1 £4.50, 72p, £10.00, £1.20; **2** 48p, 40p, £1.44, £2.58; **3** £4.80.

P84   Quantities for a recipe *12 cakes:* 100g each of flour, margarine and sugar, 2 eggs, 2 tbsp cocoa, 12 paper cases; *18 cakes:* 150g each of flour, margarine and sugar, 3 eggs, 3 tbsp cocoa, 18 paper cases.

P85   Fair play Best value: 6 rides for £8.40 (a total saving of 60p). Poorest value: 5 rides for £7.75, which is equivalent to £1.55 per ride.

P86   Proportion problems 1 $^{95}/_{100}$ or 95 people were happy; **2** $^{90}/_{100}$ = $^9/_{10}$ or 99 chairs are sound; **3** 32 ladies owned a hat; 20% = $^1/_5$ or 8 did not; **4** $^5/_{100}$ or $^1/_{20}$ of the group do not own a pet (ie 25 children).

P87   Currencies around the world Answers will vary.

P88   Swotty Simon's challenge 1 4781; **2** 7461; **3** 2835; **4** 2436; **5** 13.5; **6** 21.9; **7** 231; **8** 32.

📖 Puzzles and problems answers

1 **Robin Hood** The second and sixth targets

2 **She sell sea shells** £3.26

3 **Piggy banks** £17.06

4 **Ice dance** 1.2

5 **Sports day** Jack won and Anthony came last

6 **Walking the dog** 20 times

7 **Wipe-out** 6284 – 3729 = 2555

8 **Pharaoh puzzle**

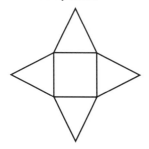

9 **Factor finder** 32 has six factors: 1, 2, 4, 8, 16, and 32

10 **Page turner** 182 pages

11 **5p and 10p** 14

12 **Kitchen floor**

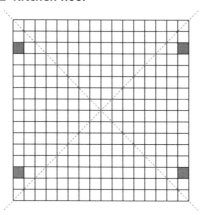

13 **Dealing with decimals** 11.4

14 **Tile trial** 8 tiles

15 **Computer games sale!** £6.19

16 **In the kitchen** Answers will vary

17 **Match the target** Answers will vary

18 **Kilos to grams** Danny is heavier by 3100g

19 **How likely?** Vicky

20 **Loaded dice** Answers will vary but must include one even number and five odd numbers

21 **All the way round** Answers will vary

22 **Happy birthday!** 10 January

23 **Up, up and away!** 6 hours and 41 minutes

24 **Kittens** 2281g or 2.281kg

25 **Measure me** 270mm

26 **Apple pie** 900g

27 **Long jump** 3.09m

28 **Pushbike puzzle** 15km

29 **Find the numbers** 9 and 6

30 **Rings of 15**

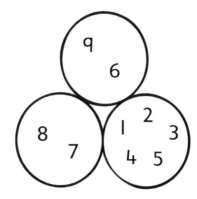

31 **Nature watch** 90 legs

32 **Maths test** Patti

33 **Javelin throw** 23.28m

34 **Pancakes** 300g flour, 6 eggs, 600ml water and 150g butter.

35 **School dinners** 108 children

36 **Skateboard scurry** 260 miles

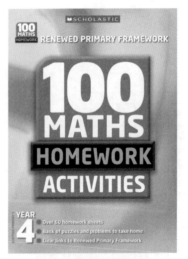
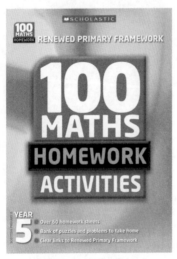